REVISE BTEC TECH AWARD
Health and Social Care (2022)

REVISION GUIDE

Series Consultant: Harry Smith

Author: Brenda Baker

A note from the publisher

While the publishers have made every attempt to ensure that advice on the qualification and its assessment is accurate, the official specification and associated assessment guidance materials are the only authoritative source of information and should always be referred to for definitive guidance.

This qualification is reviewed on a regular basis and may be updated in the future.

Any such updates that affect the content of this Revision Guide will be outlined at

www.pearsonfe.co.uk/BTECchanges. The eBook version of this Revision Guide will also be updated to reflect the latest guidance as soon as possible.

> **For the full range of Pearson revision titles across KS2, KS3, GCSE, Functional Skills, AS/A Level and BTEC visit:**
> www.pearsonschools.co.uk/revise

Published by Pearson Education Limited, 80 Strand, London WC2R ORL.

www.pearsonschoolsandfecolleges.co.uk

Text and illustrations © Pearson Education Ltd 2022
Typeset and illustrated by PDQ Media
Produced by QBS Learning
Cover illustration © Simple Line/Shutterstock

The right of Brenda Baker to be identified as author of this work has been asserted by her in accordance with the Copyright, Designs and Patents Act 1988.

First published 2022

25 24 23 22
10 9 8 7 6 5 4 3 2 1

British Library Cataloguing in Publication Data

A catalogue record for this book is available from the British Library

ISBN 978 1 292 43612 8

Acknowledgements

The author and publisher would like to thank the following individuals and organisations for permission to reproduce text, images and photographs:

Text: p23, p54 Blood Pressure Association: www.bloodpressureuk.org/BloodPressureandyou/Thebasics/Bloodpressurechart; p24, p55 **Wikimedia**: Häggström, Mikael (2014). 'Medical gallery of Mikael Häggström 2014'. *WikiJournal of Medicine* **1** (2). DOI:10.15347/wjm/2014.008. ISSN2002-4436 en.wikipedia.org/wiki/Peak_expiratory_flow#/media/File:Normal_values_for_peak_expiratory_flow_-_EU_scale.png; **p24, p55 Nunn AJ Gregg**: www.peakflow.com/pefr_normal_values.pdf; **p25 World Health Organization**: www.assessmentpsychology.com/icbmi.htm; **p25 Crown Copyright**: National Health Service: www.nhs.uk/live-well/healthy-weight/height-weight-chart: contains public sector information licensed under the Open Government Licence v3.0.

Photographs: (Key: b: bottom, c: centre; l: left; r: right; t: top) **Alamy Stock Photo**: Angela Hampton Picture Library 1, Bob Daemmrich 4, david soulsby 18cr, OJO Images Ltd 22, Science Photo Library 24, PhotoAlto sas 32, John Powell 44, **123rf**: Kaspars Grinvalds 3, Hongqi Zhang 23, Cathy Yeulet 28, Marcin Balcerzak 41, Katarzyna Białasiewicz 29, **shutterstock**: LanaElcova 17, Rudmer Zwerver 18tr, Rawpixel.com 34, Doucefleur 14.

Notes from the publisher

1. While the publishers have made every attempt to ensure that advice on the qualification and its assessment is accurate, the official specification and associated assessment guidance materials are the only authoritative source of information and should always be referred to for definitive guidance.

Pearson examiners have not contributed to any sections in this resource relevant to examination papers for which they have responsibility.

2. Pearson has robust editorial processes, including answer and fact checks, to ensure the accuracy of the content in this publication, and every effort is made to ensure this publication is free of errors. We are, however, only human, and occasionally errors do occur. Pearson is not liable for any misunderstandings that arise as a result of errors in this publication, but it is our priority to ensure that the content is accurate. If you spot an error, please do contact us at resourcescorrections@pearson.com so we can make sure it is corrected.

Websites

Pearson Education Limited is not responsible for the content of any external internet sites. It is essential for tutors to preview each website before using it in class so as to ensure that the URL is still accurate, relevant and appropriate. We suggest that tutors bookmark useful websites and consider enabling students to access them through the school/college intranet.

Introduction

Revising Component 3 of your BTEC Tech Award

This Revision Guide has been designed to support you in preparing for the externally assessed component of your course.

Component 3, Health and Wellbeing, builds on the knowledge, understanding and skills developed in Components 1 and 2. For your Component 3 assessment you will explore factors and their effects on health and wellbeing, drawing on your understanding of human development and life events from unit 1 and services, support and approaches from unit 2. You will make recommendations and suggest actions to improve the health and wellbeing of individuals. A 'Revise it!' feature shows where you are revising content from Components 1 and 2 within Component 3.

Your revision guide

This Revision Guide contains two types of pages, shown below.

Content **pages** help you revise the essential content you need to know for Component 3.

Skills **pages** help you prepare for your assessment.

Skills pages have a coloured edge and are shaded in the table of contents.

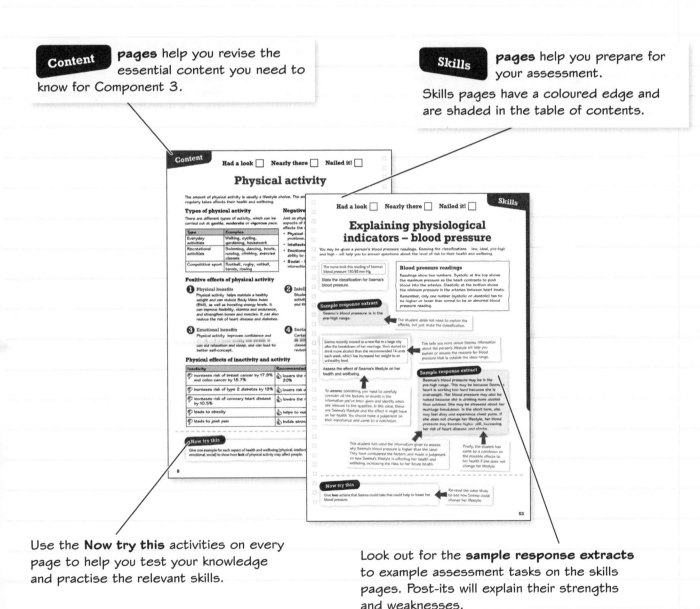

Use the **Now try this** activities on every page to help you test your knowledge and practise the relevant skills.

Look out for the **sample response extracts** to example assessment tasks on the skills pages. Post-its will explain their strengths and weaknesses.

Contents

A small bit of small print

Pearson publishes Sample Assessment Material and the Specification on its website. This is the official content and this book should be used in conjunction with it. The questions in *Now try this* have been written to help you test your knowledge and skills. Remember: the real assessment may not look like this.

Health and wellbeing

Health and wellbeing is a combination of physical health and social, emotional and intellectual (mental) wellbeing, not just the absence of disease or illness. Health professionals must understand the needs of the whole person to be able to support them.

The whole person

PIES stands for:

- Physical
- Intellectual
- Emotional
- Social.

It will help you to remember that health and wellbeing is about the **whole person**. A **holistic** approach is about meeting the needs of the whole person.

Social isolation has a negative effect on health and wellbeing.

Wellbeing comes from recognising the importance of all aspects of health.

 Physical health comes from:
- healthy body systems
- regular exercise
- a healthy diet
- regular sleep patterns
- access to shelter and warmth
- good personal hygiene

A holistic approach

 Emotional wellbeing comes from:
- feeling safe and secure
- being able to express all emotions
- knowing how to deal with negative emotions
- being respected by others
- having positive **self-concept**

 Intellectual wellbeing comes from keeping the brain healthy and active, through opportunities to:
- concentrate
- learn new skills and knowledge
- communicate
- solve problems

Social wellbeing comes from a person's relationships with others:
- friendships and other positive social relationships
- strong family relationships
- relationships as part of a social group

Now try this

Explain what is meant by a holistic approach to health and wellbeing.

The World Health Organization (WHO) states that health and wellbeing is not just the absence of disease.

Inherited conditions

Genes are inherited by children from both their birth parents. Genetic inheritance is a physical factor that can have positive and negative effects on a person's health and wellbeing.

Inherited physical characteristics

Children inherit many physical characteristics from their parents, such as height, skin and eye colour, and hair type and colour. These characteristics can affect social and emotional wellbeing because they influence a person's **self-concept**, which is composed of their:

- **self-image** (how a person sees themselves)
- **self-esteem** (how they feel about themselves).

Genes and environment

Chromosomes carry **genes** that determine aspects of a person's physical makeup. A gene is a section of DNA that carries a code. Different versions of a gene, which code for variations of the same characteristic (such as blue eyes and brown eyes), are called **alleles**.

Environmental factors, such as diet, also have an effect on physical appearance. For example, a person may not grow to their full, genetically determined height if they do not have enough food.

Inherited conditions

Sometimes genes can be faulty. Conditions may be inherited when faulty genes are passed from one parent (if dominant) or both parents (if recessive).

Condition	Cause	Effects
Cystic fibrosis	The condition may be passed on when both parents have a faulty gene. A person's ability to make a CFTR protein, which moves water in and out of cells, is affected, resulting in a build-up of thick sticky mucus in the lungs and digestive system.	A person will have breathing problems requiring regular physiotherapy. They will have an increased likelihood of lung infections and loss of appetite.
Sickle cell disease	This is more common in people with African or Caribbean backgrounds. It may be passed on when both parents have the sickle cell gene. Sickle cell is a blood disorder that affects the development of red blood cells.	Red blood cells are usually round but in sickle cells they are 'sickle' shaped (like a crescent moon). At times, these may cause painful blockages in blood vessels, referred to as 'a crisis'. Organ damage may occur.

Genetic predisposition

Some people are **predisposed** (more likely) to develop conditions because of their genetic makeup, for example heart disease, cancer and diabetes.

Whether a person *actually* develops these conditions depends on **lifestyle and environmental factors,** such as diet and exercise, air quality and level of stress.

Effects of inherited disorders

Inherited conditions can affect the whole person:

- **Physical** health – body systems, growth and mobility.
- **Intellectual** wellbeing – learning, thinking, problem solving and decision making.
- **Emotional** wellbeing – how people feel about themselves.
- **Social** wellbeing – the ability to build relationships.

Now try this

Gemma, aged 14, has the inherited condition cystic fibrosis. She has regular physiotherapy to help clear her lungs of mucus and frequently spends time in hospital.

Describe possible effects of cystic fibrosis on Gemma's physical, intellectual, emotional and social wellbeing.

As well as the physical effects, think about the impact of missing school and how Gemma feels about herself.

Physical ill health

Physical ill health refers to illnesses and disorders which negatively affect a person's body systems. Common conditions that can cause ill health are cardiovascular disease, obesity and type 2 diabetes.

Cardiovascular system

The cardiovascular system refers to the heart, blood vessels and blood that is circulated around the body. When the heart does not function effectively it can cause disease.

Coronary heart disease is one of the main causes of death. It is caused by a build-up of fatty deposits in the arteries around the heart that may result in:

- heart attacks caused by blockage in blood flow
- angina, causing pain or shortness of breath when blood flow is restricted
- heart failure when the heart can no longer pump blood around the body.

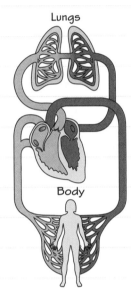

Lungs

Body

☐ Oxygen-poor, carbon dioxide-rich blood

■ Oxygen-rich, carbon dioxide-poor blood

Strokes happen when the blood supply to the brain is cut off temporarily. This can cause muscle weakness or paralysis in one side of the body or even death.

Peripheral arterial disease is caused by a build-up of fatty deposits in the arteries of the legs. It causes pain, potential ulcers or weakness.

Type 2 diabetes

Type 2 diabetes is a serious and common condition. The condition occurs when the pancreas is not working properly and cannot make enough insulin. This causes the blood sugar levels to rise.

Symptoms include tiredness, urinating more regularly and excessive thirst. High blood sugar levels over time can cause damage to eyes, feet or the heart.

Risk factors

In 2019, in the UK there were around 4 million people with type 2 diabetes. (NICE, 2020)

Individuals are more likely to experience type 2 diabetes if they are:

- overweight or obese
- have a family history of the disease
- are of black African, Caribbean, or South Asian descent.

Obesity

People who are very overweight are described as obese. An NHS report (2020) shows more than half of adults in the UK are overweight or obese and 20% of year 6 children.

Obesity is often caused when the body stores excess energy as body fat because a person:

- eats more calories than the body needs
- does not take exercise to burn off body fat.

Impacts on health and wellbeing

- breathlessness
- sweating
- low self-esteem
- difficulty in carrying out tasks
- higher risk of serious conditions such as heart disease, type 2 diabetes and high blood pressure.

Now try this

Name **three** of the possible effects of coronary heart disease.

 Fatty deposits prevent the blood from flowing properly.

Mental ill health

Mental health describes a person's psychological and emotional wellbeing. Events and circumstances that happen can cause mental ill health effects, such as anxiety and stress.

Effects of mental ill health

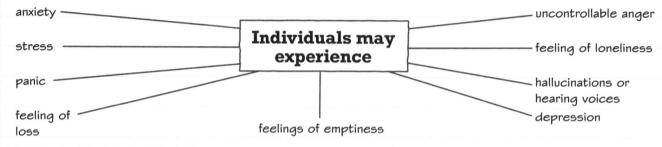

anxiety — uncontrollable anger

stress — feeling of loneliness

panic — hallucinations or hearing voices

feeling of loss — depression

Individuals may experience

feelings of emptiness

Anxiety and stress

Stress happens when people experience:

- pressures at work
- exams
- financial difficulties
- life events and circumstances such as illness, relationship changes (marriage, divorce), moving home or bereavement.

Response

The body's response to stressful situations is a rise in the hormones cortisol and adrenaline (triggering the fight-or-flight response). Low-level or short-term stress can be positive, helping people to function better by boosting their concentration and thinking skills. Intense stress or stress over a longer period has negative, unhealthy effects on the body.

Effects of mental ill health on health and wellbeing

Physical	Increased heartbeat
	Muscle tension
	High blood pressure
	Heart disease
	Digestive problems
	Headaches
	Poor sleep patterns
Intellectual health	Poor concentration
	Forgetfulness
Emotional health	Difficulty controlling emotions – crying or getting angry
	Feeling insecure
	Negative self-concept
	Feeling anxious and frightened
Social	Isolation
	Breakdown of relationships or friendships

Now try this

Identify a situation in which you felt stressed, for example before an exam or when you experienced a challenging life event. List the effects it had on you.

Consider physical, intellectual, emotional and social effects.

Physical abilities

Physical abilities describe how well a person can move and complete actions using their body strength and stamina; this determines how they carry out their daily life.

Physical skills

- Balance – ability to remain steady and control body movements.
- Strength – having power in muscles and joints to lift and move objects.
- Mobility – ability to move joints and muscles to move around freely.
- Stamina – sustained physical activity.
- Flexibility – ability to bend and twist.
- Fine motor skills – making movements in fingers, wrists and hands.

Strength, stamina, balance and flexibility are all important to play sports.

Effects of physical ability

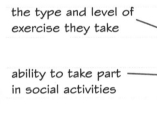

the type and level of exercise they take

ability to undertake housework and everyday chores

ability to take part in social activities

A person's physical abilities determine

their choice of work and how they carry it out

ability to carry out their own personal care

ability to carry out 'tricky' tasks such as opening jars, fastening buttons, sewing and tying laces

Physical disability

This is a term used to describe conditions that affect part of a person's body, limiting their mobility and the functions of their body. It might be hereditary, acquired through accident or injury, or because of the ageing process.

Physical disability does not necessarily mean a person is not able to carry out tasks. They may need more time, support or equipment.

The impact of a physical disability

The loss of physical capacity results in the person having a reduced ability, or inability, to perform body movements. It may affect:

- standing or walking
- strength and stamina
- moving hands and arms
- control of muscles
- the use of small muscles in fingers.

Now try this

Give **two** examples of how difficulties in using small muscles in the fingers may impact on a person's daily life.

Think about the tasks you would find difficult if you didn't have flexibility or strength in your fingers.

Sensory impairment

Sensory impairment means the loss or partial loss of one of the senses: sight, hearing, smell or taste.

Types of visual impairment

1 Partially sighted – a degree of sight loss that cannot be rectified by glasses or contact lenses

2 Blindness – a total loss of sight

Causes

Causes of visual impairment may include:
- inherited conditions
- illness related, for example diabetes
- injury, for example work or sports
- age-related conditions such as macular degeneration or cataracts.

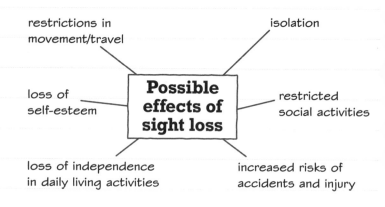

restrictions in movement/travel

isolation

loss of self-esteem

Possible effects of sight loss

restricted social activities

loss of independence in daily living activities

increased risks of accidents and injury

Types of hearing impairment or loss

1 Hearing impairment – when there is difficulty hearing

2 Hearing loss – when a person cannot hear sounds and it cannot be rectified by hearing aids

Causes

Causes of hearing impairment may include:
- inherited conditions
- injuries
- infection
- noise induced, for example machinery, music
- age-related loss.

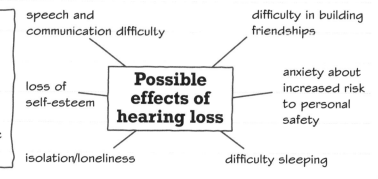

speech and communication difficulty

difficulty in building friendships

loss of self-esteem

Possible effects of hearing loss

anxiety about increased risk to personal safety

isolation/loneliness

difficulty sleeping

Loss of taste and smell

The loss of taste and smell is often temporary but may be caused by:
- a virus or infection, for example coronavirus
- allergies
- polyps in the nose
- smoking
- drugs
- ageing.

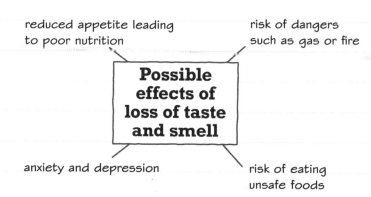

reduced appetite leading to poor nutrition

risk of dangers such as gas or fire

Possible effects of loss of taste and smell

anxiety and depression

risk of eating unsafe foods

Now try this

Give **two** reasons why a person with hearing impairment may experience isolation.

Social isolation means having a feeling of not belonging.

Nutrition

Good nutrition provided by a balanced diet is essential to maintain health and wellbeing.

Quality of foods and nutrients

Fresh, unprocessed foods are the most beneficial and contain the most nutrients. The table shows the major nutrients found in each food group.

Food group	Main nutrients
Fruit and vegetables	Vitamins, minerals
Starchy foods	Carbohydrates, minerals, vitamins
Meat, fish, eggs, pulses	Protein, fats, iron (mineral)
Dairy products	Protein, fats, vitamins, calcium (mineral)
Oils	Fats

Positive effects of nutrients

This table shows how different nutrients contribute to physical health and wellbeing.

Nutrient	Purpose
Vitamins	Healthy immune system, skin and eyes
Carbohydrates	Boost energy levels
Protein	Growth and repair of tissues
Minerals	Healthy teeth, blood, skin and hair
Fats	Energy, healthy cell structure, help vitamin absorption

Negative effects of nutrient deficiency

A lack of certain nutrients may lead to illnesses such as:

- anaemia (reduced numbers of red blood cells)
- rickets (a bone disease)
- poor growth
- depression
- tiredness
- excessive weight loss.

Negative effects of excess nutrients

A person who is obese (very overweight) may:

- be more prone to illnesses such as diabetes, heart disease, high blood pressure, cancer and strokes
- have reduced life expectancy
- be less able to undertake physical activity
- have poor self-concept.

Maintaining a healthy weight

- People who take in as much energy as they use maintain a **healthy weight**.
- Those who eat an excess of energy-containing foods gain weight, become overweight and may eventually become **obese**.
- Those whose energy consumption is less than they need may **lose weight**.

Very muscular people may weigh more than expected for their height, but they are fit. They may require a high-energy diet if they do a lot of exercise.

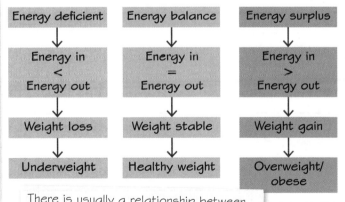

There is usually a relationship between energy intake, energy use and weight.

Give **three** ways eating fresh fruits and vegetables contributes to health and wellbeing.

 Re-read the two tables above.

Physical activity

Physical activity is usually a lifestyle choice. The amount of physical activity a person regularly takes affects their health and wellbeing.

Types of physical activity

There are different types of activity, which can be carried out at **gentle**, **moderate** or **vigorous** pace.

Type	Examples
Everyday activities	Walking, cycling, gardening, housework
Recreational activities	Swimming, dancing, bowls, running, climbing, exercise classes
Competitive sport	Football, rugby, netball, tennis, rowing

Negative effects of not being active

Just as physical activity has positive effects on all aspects of health and wellbeing, not being active affects the whole person negatively:

- **Physical** – obesity and associated health problems.
- **Intellectual** – reduced brain performance.
- **Emotional** – poor self-concept and reduced ability to cope with stress.
- **Social** – fewer opportunities for social interaction.

Positive effects of physical activity

1 Physical benefits

Physical activity helps maintain a healthy weight and can reduce Body Mass Index (BMI), as well as boosting energy levels. It can improve flexibility, stamina and endurance, and strengthen bones and muscles. It can also reduce the risk of heart disease and diabetes.

2 Intellectual benefits

Studies show a link between levels of physical activity and brain function, such as memory and thinking skills, at every stage of life.

3 Emotional benefits

Physical activity improves confidence and mood, and reduces anxiety and stress. It can aid relaxation and sleep, and can lead to better self-concept.

4 Social benefits

Certain types of physical activity (such as competitive sports, dance or exercise classes) encourage social interaction, reducing isolation and improving social skills.

Physical effects of inactivity and activity

Inactivity	Recommended level of activity
increases risk of breast cancer by 17.9% and colon cancer by 18.7%	lowers the risk of breast and colon cancer by 20%
increases risk of type 2 diabetes by 13%	lowers risk of developing type 2 diabetes by 40%
increases risk of coronary heart disease by 10.5%	lowers the risk of heart disease by 35%
leads to obesity	helps to maintain a healthy weight
leads to joint pain	builds strong bones and healthy muscles

Now try this

Give **one** example for each aspect of health and wellbeing (physical, intellectual, emotional, social) to show how a **lack** of physical activity may affect people.

People who are not physically active will not experience the positive effects outlined on this page.

Smoking and nicotine use

Smoking and the use of nicotine is a lifestyle choice. Nicotine is an addictive drug. It is found in tobacco products such as cigarettes, cigars and chewing tobacco. These products carry a health warning as they can have serious effects on health and wellbeing.

Harmful chemicals

Cigarette smoke contains harmful chemicals that are absorbed in the lungs.

- **Nicotine** causes addiction, raised pulse rate and blood pressure, and thrombosis (blood clots).
- **Tar** causes cancers of the nose, throat, tongue, lungs, stomach and bladder.
- **Carbon monoxide** reduces the amount of oxygen in the blood, straining the heart.
- **Soot** particles cause bronchitis and emphysema.

Reasons people smoke

People give different reasons for smoking, often related to the **addictive** nature of nicotine, such as:

- feeling unable to quit
- to overcome addictions to other drugs or alcohol
- to relieve stress and relax
- because friends smoke (peer pressure)
- to reward themselves
- a fear of putting on weight (nicotine stops people feeling hungry).

Negative effects of smoking

 Physical

Smoking increases the risk of life-threatening diseases such as lung cancer, stroke, coronary heart disease, emphysema, bronchitis and pneumonia. Smoking during pregnancy carries an increased risk of having a low birth weight baby, or a premature birth or stillbirth.

 Intellectual

Addiction to nicotine causes cravings, irritation, distraction and stress when the smoker is unable to smoke. Smokers are more likely to develop depression and anxiety over time.

 Emotional

Being unable to quit smoking may lead to poor self-concept. Smokers may worry about the negative effects on their health and about the cost of cigarettes. Research data shows that smoking is associated with poor mental health.

 Social

Smokers may feel socially excluded when they have to leave social spaces to smoke outside. People may avoid smokers because of the smell of their hair, breath and clothes.

Passive smoking

Breathing in the smoke from other people's cigarettes carries some of the same risks as smoking. In the UK, smoking is banned in all public indoor spaces and some public outdoor spaces, and it is illegal to smoke in a car in the company of someone who is under 18. This protects people against passive smoking.

Other nicotine products

Smokeless tobacco, nasal snuff or chewing tobacco is absorbed through the membranes of the nose and mouth. It can cause oral cancer and gum disease, as well as increasing the risk of heart disease.

Recently, people have been using 'electronic cigarettes' to inhale nicotine (vaping). The long-term health effects are not yet known.

Now try this

Write a short paragraph to explain why smoking can have negative emotional and social impacts on health and wellbeing.

 Remember, an emotional effect is about feelings and a social effect is about how you relate to others.

Alcohol misuse

The consumption of alcohol is a lifestyle choice. Its misuse can have a negative effect on health and wellbeing. Learn about recommended levels of alcohol consumption on page 28.

Alcohol misuse

Alcohol misuse is when a person:

- regularly drinks more than the recommended level
- makes decisions and actions that are negativity affected by their alcohol consumption
- becomes dependent on alcohol (they are not in control of their drinking)
- binge drinks (consumes a large amount of alcohol over a short period of time).

Short-term impact of alcohol misuse

Drinking more than recommended levels of alcohol may lead to:

👎 becoming aggressive or violent

👎 lack of concentration

👎 trips and falls, causing injury

👎 hangovers (headaches, dizziness, dehydration)

👎 making poor judgements such as having unprotected sex, drunk driving.

1 Physical: diseases of the major organs (liver, heart, kidneys); cancer (mouth, throat, oesophagus, breast); stroke; stomach ulcers; weight gain; infertility /impotence

2 Emotional: low self-concept; personality change; addiction (alcoholism)

Negative effects of drinking more than recommended levels

3 Mental wellbeing: depression and anxiety; self-harm; brain damage; impaired brain development of an unborn child; poor decision-making

4 Social: breakdown of relationships; domestic abuse; social exclusion

5 Economic: job loss; inability to manage money

Drinking heavily in pregnancy can cause foetal alcohol syndrome (restricted growth, facial abnormalities, behavioural disorders) in a baby.

Now try this

Carrie drinks more than the recommended level of alcohol when she goes out in the evening and often has hangovers the next morning.

Give **three** examples of the possible effects on her ability to work.

Try to include at least one short-term and one long-term example.

Substance misuse

All drug use has an effect on health and wellbeing. Drugs include legal substances such as nicotine, alcohol, prescription and over-the-counter medicines, and illegal substances such as cannabis and cocaine. Substance misuse has a negative effect on health and wellbeing.

Prescription drugs

Prescription drugs are those recommended by a doctor or practice nurse. When taken correctly, they have beneficial effects on health and wellbeing, such as reducing pain or fighting infection.

Their misuse can have negative effects on health and wellbeing.

Misuse of prescription drugs

The use of prescription drugs must be monitored by a health practitioner. Prescription drugs are misused when people:

- take them for non-medical (recreational) reasons
- become addicted to them
- take more or less than the prescribed dose
- take drugs that belong to another person.

Negative effects of substance misuse on mental health

The three main types of recreational drugs are shown in the table. All are **addictive**.

People take these to change their mental state. Some drugs may give an immediate feeling of wellbeing, or even euphoria, but all have longer-term negative effects on mental health.

Cannabis / Marijuana may act as a stimulant or depressant

Drug type	Possible short-term effects	Possible long-term effects
Stimulants nicotine, cocaine, caffeine, cannabis	Increase brain activity, blood pressure and heart rate making individuals more active, alert, excited	Paranoia, aggressiveness, schizophrenia, depression, suicidal feelings
Depressants alcohol, solvents, heroin	Calm, relaxed, reduced tension, confusion and loss of concentration	Sleep problems, anxiety, memory loss, depression
Hallucinogens LSD, ketamine	Hallucinations, altered sense of space and time, thoughts and feelings, and moods	Anxiety, memory loss, depression, panic attacks, flashbacks

Other negative effects of substance misuse

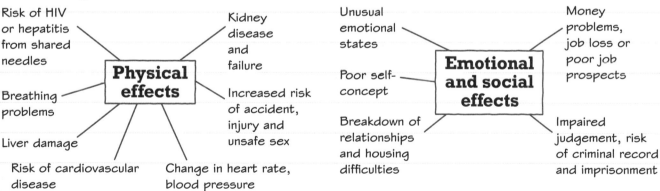

Physical effects:
- Risk of HIV or hepatitis from shared needles
- Breathing problems
- Liver damage
- Risk of cardiovascular disease
- Change in heart rate, blood pressure
- Increased risk of accident, injury and unsafe sex
- Kidney disease and failure

Emotional and social effects:
- Unusual emotional states
- Poor self-concept
- Breakdown of relationships and housing difficulties
- Money problems, job loss or poor job prospects
- Impaired judgement, risk of criminal record and imprisonment

Now try this

Liam, 16, has recently started taking stimulant drugs as a result of peer pressure.

Give **two** possible effects on his emotional and/or social wellbeing.

Think about how drug use may affect his behaviour and the impact this has on his relationships.

Relationships

Social factors such as relationships and social interaction may positively or negatively affect health and wellbeing.

Types of relationship

Relationships can be **formal** (such as between work colleagues) or **informal** (such as between friends and family).

REVISE IT!
You might need to use Component 1 knowledge about social factors in your assessment

Positive effects of relationships

Relationship	Possible effects
Close friendships	From around the age of three, children start to build friendships outside the family group. These can: • give feelings of security and confidence • promote positive self-concept • provide encouragement to take part in leisure and physical activities.
Family relationships	Close family relationships can provide: • unconditional love, which benefits self-concept • security and support • encouragement to learn and develop new skills • shared family, social and leisure experiences • confidence to build relationships with others.
Peers	Building relationships with people of similar interests: • may support life choices • extends a social circle • means there is someone outside the family to share worries or concerns.
Colleagues	Relationships with colleagues can: • help to develop skills and working practices • increase job satisfaction • build team spirit and sense of belonging.

Unsupportive relationships

Unsupportive relationships may result in:

👎 negaitve self-concept

👎 feelings of hurt, loneliness and distrust

👎 difficulties in building relationships

👎 lack of independence.

Relationship breakdown

Friendships and relationships can break down. This may adversely affect health and wellbeing.

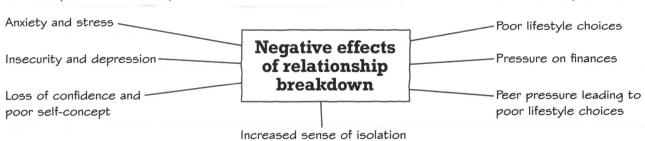

Anxiety and stress — **Negative effects of relationship breakdown** — Poor lifestyle choices

Insecurity and depression — Pressure on finances

Loss of confidence and poor self-concept — Peer pressure leading to poor lifestyle choices

Increased sense of isolation

Now try this

Give examples of how your own relationships have had positive effects on your health and wellbeing.

You might like to think about how you have benefited from relationships with family or friends.

Social interaction

Social interaction is the process of acting and reacting to people around us by communicating and forming relationships.

Social inclusion

Inclusion happens when people feel they belong to a social group such as:

- family members and friends
- work colleagues
- school or college learners
- members of interest groups
- community members, such as members of a church or cultural group.

Social exclusion

Exclusion happens when people do not have regular contact with others. This may be because a person:

- has difficulty in communicating with others if they have a mental or physical illness, or a condition that affects communication
- has experienced life changes such as bereavement or relationship breakdown
- is homeless.

Discrimination

Discrimination is the unjust treatment of a person because of a characteristic they possess such as race, age, sex, gender reassignment, disability, sexual orientation, religion, pregnancy and marriage or civil partnership. The Equality Act (2010) identifies four types of discrimination.

Type	What it means	Example
Direct discrimination	Treating someone differently because of a characteristic such as age or race	Not being considered for promotion because of age or race
Indirect discrimination	When individuals are put at a disadvantage because of a characteristic such as sex or religion	A dress code introduced that does not allow a head covering
Harassment and bullying	Being picked on, experiencing abusive, bullying or unwanted behaviour	Being mocked directly or through social media because of gender reassignment or sexual orientation
Victimisation	Receiving unfair treatments because of something they do or say	Being excluded from a social event at work after making a complaint about the actions of a colleague

Types of bullying

Bullying can happen at any age group from childhood to adulthood.

- Verbal: name calling, threats, sexist or anti-racial comments
- Cyberbullying: sending hurtful comments, sharing private information or photos
- Physical: pinching, hitting, kicking, slapping
- Emotional: spreading rumours, exclusion from a group

 1 Social isolation – anxiety, depression, low self-esteem, poorer school grades

 3 Financial – access to jobs and promotion

Effects of discrimination and bullying

2 Life opportunities – access to social activity, higher education

 4 Access – to health and social care services

Now try this

Suggest **one** more example for each of the four types of discrimination.

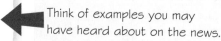 Think of examples you may have heard about on the news.

Cultural factors

REVISE IT!
You might need to use Component 1 knowledge about cultural factors in your assessment

Cultural factors can affect people's lifestyle, beliefs, attitudes and access to health and social care.

Cultural factors that can impact negatively on health and wellbeing

Religion	• Some religious beliefs may impact on a person's unease about accepting some healthcare interventions, so conditions are left untreated. • A person may face discrimination, leading to anxiety. • They may face barriers in accessing health and social care because of cultural beliefs or traditions, language, religious practices or diet being misunderstood, leading to conditions going undiagnosed and untreated.
Gender expectations	• Imposed gender roles influence attitudes to lifestyle. • The gender pay gap means women are economically worse off than men, which may affect areas such as diet or housing. • Men are seen as the 'stronger sex' so may be reluctant to seek treatment. • A person may be reluctant about being examined by a health worker of a different sex.
Gender identity	• This is how a person identifies internally and chooses to express themselves to others. • Their identity may be questioned by family, friends or professional health workers, potentially causing mental ill health. • They may be reluctant to seek help or may face discrimination when accessing health care services so do not get or seek the treatment they need.
Sexual orientation	• This describes who a person is attracted to – the same sex (gay, homosexual, lesbian), a different sex (straight, heterosexual) or both (bisexual). • A person may be discriminated against because of their orientation and feel excluded, causing anxiety or depression. • They may be reluctant to seek help or face barriers so conditions are not diagnosed or untreated.

Positive factors

A person may:

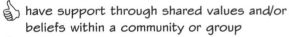 have support through shared values and/or beliefs within a community or group

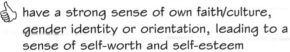 have a strong sense of own faith/culture, gender identity or orientation, leading to a sense of self-worth and self-esteem

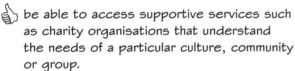 be able to access supportive services such as charity organisations that understand the needs of a particular culture, community or group.

Community participation

Community means a group with which a person identifies. It could be their location or a particular cultural group.

Positive effects

👍 Participation brings a sense of belonging and well-being.

👍 People can be supportive.

Lack of community participation can lead to:

👎 isolation

👎 reluctance to ask for help.

Now try this

Studies have shown that men are less likely to seek help from healthcare professionals than women.

Give **two** reasons why a man may be more reluctant to seek help.

 Consider the cultural factors above to help you answer this question.

Economic factors

Economic factors relate to a person's employment situation and financial resources. Economic factors can determine a person's and their family's lifestyle, which may positively or negatively affect health and wellbeing.

Employment situation

This describes different employment situations that may impact on a person's finances.

- Employed – part-time or full-time, self-employed, working for a company or individual
- Unemployed – not able to find work, made redundant, unable to work because of family commitments or a disability

Finances can also be affected by a person's occupation, job role, job status, level of responsibility or expertise.

REVISE IT!
You might need to use this Component 1 knowledge in your assessment

Financial resources

This describes the money and personal wealth that a person has at their disposal.

- Income – money that a person receives at regular intervals such as a salary; pensions; allowances such as universal credit, carers' allowance; income from investments
- Inheritance – money or other assets such as property or jewellery that is left to a person after the death of another
- Savings – money that is set aside, often in banks, to spend on something specific or for the future

Poverty

People with limited financial resources live in **absolute poverty** without money to meet basic needs.

People with reduced financial resources live in **relative poverty** and can only pay for basic needs.

Effects of economic factors on health and wellbeing

Aspect	Positive effects	Negative effects
Physical	👍 A higher income can result in good housing conditions. 👍 A higher income can provide a healthier diet.	👎 A lack of income can lead to poor, damp housing that can lead to lung conditions. 👎 Being unable to afford sufficient food can lead to a lack of essential nutrients, resulting in ill health.
Intellectual	👍 A higher income can result in more leisure time for intellectual activities. 👍 Work, education or training helps to develop problem-solving and thinking skills.	👎 Some people work very long hours to improve their financial position, leading to less leisure time and reduced learning opportunities. 👎 Being unemployed can result in poor mental health.
Emotional	👍 A well-paid job gives a feeling of security. 👍 Being financially secure promotes positive self-concept.	👎 Financial worries can result in stress and breakdown of relationships. 👎 Unemployment or low-status work can lead to low self-concept.
Social	👍 A higher income provides more opportunities for socialising, travel and leisure pursuits. 👍 Work gives opportunities for socialising with colleagues.	👎 Lack of financial resources reduces opportunities for socialising. 👎 Unemployment reduces opportunities for relationships, leading to social isolation.

Now try this

Explain, giving **two** reasons, why a person's occupational and employment statuses can affect their emotional development.

Give reasons for your answer, making links to positive and negative effects.

Environmental factors – housing

Housing is an environmental factor. The quality of the home in which a person lives is an important factor in determining their health and wellbeing. Look at page 18 for more on the home environment.

Good living conditions

Good housing has a positive effect on health and wellbeing. It is often:

- located in areas with less pollution
- quiet and safe
- spacious
- warm and dry
- close to or has safe outdoor space.

> **REVISE IT!**
> You might need to use this Component 1 knowledge about environmental factors in your assessment.

Poor living conditions

Poor housing has negative effects on health and wellbeing.

Condition	Effects on health and wellbeing
Damp and mould spores	Respiratory (breathing) problems, for example asthma
Overcrowding	Anxiety and depression, difficulty concentrating and studying, sleeplessness, pressure on relationships, leading to arguments
No open spaces	Physically less fit because of lack of exercise and physical play
Poor heating	Poor health (colds, flu), heart disease
Vermin	Rats carry a bacterial infection affecting the organs of the body (Weil's disease); cockroaches trigger asthma and allergies and carry diseases

Comparing the city to the countryside

There are pros and cons to living in either a city or a rural location.

City locations

👍 Better transport links

👍 Close to facilities like shops, sports centres, libraries, theatres, museums

👍 Easy access to social events

👍 Close to health and social care services

👎 Polluted (air, noise, light)

👎 Some people may feel isolated

Rural locations

👍 Sense of community

👍 Access to outdoors and fresh air

👎 Long commutes to work

👎 More difficult to access health and social care services

👎 Some people may feel isolated

Now try this

Use the information about negative effects of housing from this page and sort them under the headings **Physical**, **Intellectual**, **Emotional** and **Social**.

 Use the table on this page to help you.

Environmental factors – pollution

Environmental factors refer to the air, water and land around us. Pollution in the environment affects health and wellbeing.

Pollution

Pollution is the **contamination** of the environment (air, water, land) and living organisms by harmful chemicals. Noise and light pollution also affect health and wellbeing.

One type of pollution is outdoor air pollution. Research shows that outdoor air pollution causes 40 000 deaths each year in the UK. Children and older people are most at risk from the negative effects.

Types of pollution

Type	Causes
Outdoor air pollution	Chemicals from factories, particles and nitrogen dioxide from vehicle exhausts
Indoor air pollution	Aerosols (deodorants and cleaning products), mould spores, cigarette smoke, carbon monoxide from faulty boilers
Water pollution	Farm fertilisers and pesticides, factory waste, sewage leaks
Land contamination	Landfill, intensive farming resulting in soil pollution
Food pollutants	Pesticides and fertilisers, and chemicals used in food processing
Noise pollution	Machinery, traffic, loud music
Light pollution	Excessive artificial light, for example street lights at night

Negative effects of pollutants

Chemical pollutants are taken into the human body through the nose, mouth or skin.

During pregnancy – low birth weight or premature birth

Reduction of brain function – thinking skills and memory

Lung damage – asthma, bronchitis, lung cancer

Negative effects

Heart damage – heart disease, stroke

Allergies – rashes, wheezing, allergic rhinitis

Effects of noise pollution

- Stress
- High blood pressure
- Hearing loss
- Disrupted sleep

Now try this

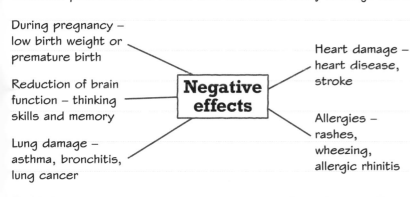

Neville is 82. He used to live in a large city and worked in a car repair shop, but retired to the country. Neville has never smoked although his wife used to. He has been diagnosed with chronic bronchitis.

Remember that, although the environment Neville lives in now may be healthy, the pollution he breathed in earlier may have had a long-lasting effect.

Explain **two** likely causes of Neville's bronchitis.

The home environment

The home environment can be unsafe for children and vulnerable adults. Experiences of conflict between others or abuse towards themselves can cause a significant negative impact on health and wellbeing.

Parental conflict

Some children see and experience a high level of domestic conflict including arguing and physical attacks between adults in the family. It can be extremely frightening, affecting their short- and long-term health and wellbeing.

The impact may be:

- frequent physical symptoms such as headache or stomach ache
- being withdrawn
- being aggressive themselves
- inability to sleep because of noise/arguments.

Positive home environment

A good home environment can mean:

👍 good physical health because of caring relationships

👍 less chance of accident or injury due to being in a safe environment

👍 positive emotional wellbeing because of supportive relationships

👍 better able to concentrate on activities because of calm surroundings.

Abuse

Abuse is something that can happen towards children or adults. It can happen to individuals because they are vulnerable (more easily hurt or abused), such as individuals with learning or physical disabilities or older people.

Types of abuse

There are different types of abuse including:

- physical (such as hitting or slapping)
- emotional (such as being frightened or frequently criticised)
- sexual (such as being forced or coerced into sexual acts or exposure to sexual materials)
- neglect (not receiving the care needed such as being loved, having suitable clothing, food or warmth).

Financial abuse

This type of abuse happens to adults. It describes when money is taken from them by someone in the home or someone that comes into their home. It can cause confusion and anxiety. A loss of finances may mean that a person is unable to buy healthy food or heat their home, leading to physical illnesses.

The possible impact of abuse

👎 Being withdrawn

👎 Being aggressive

👎 Having difficulty sleeping

👎 Being frightened or anxious

👎 Likelihood of frequent infections or being underweight if neglected

👎 Being physically hurt may result in burns, bruising or broken bones

👎 Low self-esteem and self-concept

👎 Displaying physical symptoms such as headache or stomach ache

Permanent injuries from physical abuse caused by broken bones, scalds or burns

Inability to form friendships and relationships in adulthood

Making poor life choices such as drug or alcohol misuse

The long-term impact of abuse

Malnutrition or obesity through neglect

Physical abuse may cause permanent brain damage or death

Having delayed or restricted development

Mental health conditions

Now try this

Why might a teacher suspect that a pupil is experiencing parental conflict or abuse in their home? Give **three** signs they may observe.

 Think about the signs that are easy to spot by a teacher.

Life events

As people move through life, events happen that impact on their health and wellbeing. There may be physical events or relationship changes.

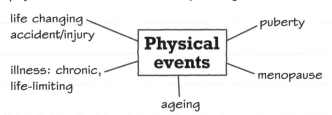

life changing accident/injury

illness: chronic, life-limiting

Physical events

puberty

menopause

ageing

Expected or unexpected

Some life events, such as ageing or puberty, are expected. Others, such as injury or an illness, are unexpected and cannot be predicted. As it is not possible to prepare for these events, they often have a greater impact on health and wellbeing.

Injury or accident

These are events that can suddenly change a person's life and cause:

- physical impact; such as restricted movement, pain
- emotional impact; depression/lack of interest, isolation, loss of self-esteem
- intellectual impact; decision making.

REVISE IT!
You might need to use Component 1 knowledge about life events in your assessment.

There are also positive effects as people move to a new stage in life.

Physical life changes

Puberty, menopause and ageing cause physical changes and impact health and wellbeing.

Puberty:

- physical impact
  - physical pains
  - physical changes
  - height and muscle growth
- emotional impact
  - anxiety and depression
  - greater sense of self
  - moodiness
- intellectual effects:
  - loss of interest
  - brain development
  - new opportunities

Menopause:

- physical impact
  - hot flushes
  - headaches
  - increased risk of heart disease and osteoporosis
  - periods stop/ reduced risk of pregnancy
- emotional impact
  - stress and anxiety
- intellectual effects
  - 'brain fog'
  - forgetfulness

Ageing:

- physical impact
  - reduced mobility
  - higher risk of illness, e.g. diabetes, cancer, heart disease
- emotional impact
  - loss of independence
  - less work-related stress (retirement)
- intellectual effects
  - decline in memory/ risk of dementia

Relationship changes

- Marriage or entering a new partnership
- Divorce or ending of partnership
- Breakdown of relationships: with family, peers, friends, colleagues
- Bereavement of a close relative, partner, friend

Grief

The death of someone close may cause grief. Grief causes intense feelings of sadness, despair and isolation. A person may have a loss of appetite and lose weight. They may turn to drink or drugs.

The impact of life events

Positive impact

Entering a new partnership or marriage and making new friends and relationships can:

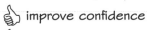 improve confidence

 build self-esteem

👍 increase feeling of security.

Negative impact

A breakdown of relationships may cause:

👎 emotional difficulties: anxiety, depression, use of alcohol, smoking or drugs

👎 social effects: isolation, loss of social contacts

👎 physical illness: headaches, digestive problems, lower immune system causing frequent colds or flu.

Now try this

Krysta, aged 67, lives with her husband Stefan and they are both retired. She has two children and three grandchildren.

Explain **one** possible positive and **one** possible negative impact of ageing on Krysta's health and wellbeing.

It is often easy to think of the negatives of ageing, but think of the positives that retirement might bring too.

Life circumstances

Circumstances change as people move through life and can impact health and wellbeing.

- **Employment status**: type of work, employment, promotion, redundancy

- **Living conditions/housing**: changes in level of security, quality of housing, level of deprivation, homelessness

Circumstances that can change

- **Education**: starting/moving school, college, university

- **Exclusion**: from a group, school or college

- **Income**: a change in level of income

- **Imprisonment**

- **Retirement**: when you stop or reduce work

The impact of life circumstances

	Positive impact of good or improved circumstances	Negative impact of poor or reduced circumstances

Employment status	• Emotional impact
	  o develops independence
	  o improves self-concept
	• Intellectual impact
	  o improves thought processes (creative thinking, problem solving)
		• Emotional impact
		  o low status roles or redundancy leads to stress and anxiety
		  o sleeplessness
		• Social impact
		  o negative or breakdown of relationships

Retirement	• Emotional impact
	  o reduced stress
	• Social impact
	  o more time to socialise with family and friends
	  o opportunities for leisure or physical activities
		• Physical impact
		  o loss of fitness and mobility if less active
		• Social impact
		  o loss of relationships with colleagues
		• Intellectual impact
		  o loss of intellectual stimulation and job status

Living conditions	• Physical impact
	  o good or improved health
	• Social impact
	  o opportunity to relax and be physically active
		• Physical impact
		  o poor health
		  o respiratory disease
		  o heart disease
		• Emotional impact
		  o isolation

Starting school, college or university	• Emotional impact
	  o improved confidence, self-esteem
	• Social impact
	  o opportunity to build new friendships
	• Intellectual impact
	  o opportunity to extend knowledge and learning, develop new skills
		• Emotional impact
		  o anxiety about new routines and meeting new people
		• Social impact
		  o insecurity about leaving parents and other familiar people

Exclusion		• Emotional impact
		  o low self-image
		• Social impact
		  o loss of friendships/social activities

Income	• Emotional impact
	  o more independence
	  o higher self-esteem
		• Physical impact
		  o poorer diet/nutrition, weight gain or loss
		• Emotional impact
		  o worry/anxiety

Imprisonment	Prison is punitive but also redemptive; many people change their lives for the better through the forced structure that prison creates.	• Emotional impact
		  o loss of independence, anxiety/depression
		• Social impact
		  o breakdown in relationships

Now try this

Write down some of your own life experiences, then identify how changes in your circumstances may have impacted on your own health and wellbeing.

You might think about how starting school or moving house affected you.

Health indicators

Health professionals measure a range of indicators to assess risks to health and wellbeing. Indicators may be physiological measurements such as blood pressure.

Indicators

Indicators may be **physiological**, such as:

- resting heart rate (pulse)
- heart rate (pulse) recovery after exercise
- blood pressure
- Body Mass Index (BMI).

Physiological indicators

Physiological indicators show how well the body's systems are functioning. Health professionals check a person's health by taking measurements. They compare the results with published guidance from reliable sources such as the National Health Service (NHS), Royal College of Nursing or charities such as the British Heart Foundation or Asthma UK.

Importance of understanding indicators

Measuring and monitoring indicators helps health professionals to:

- detect health problems at an early stage
- track improvements or deterioration in health
- make recommendations about health and treatments
- give advice about future health risks
- support individuals to make different lifestyle choices.

You will revise more about physiological indicators on pages 22–23.

Measuring physiological indicators

 Resting heart rate (pulse)

Measures the number of heart contractions in one minute.

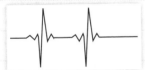

 Heart rate (pulse) – recovery after exercise

Measures the difference between the heart rate (pulse) at the end of physical activity and one minute after.

 Blood pressure

Measures the pressure of blood as it circulates in the body.

 BMI

Indicates proportion of body fat using measurements of a person's height and weight.

Now try this

Milena, aged 26, has been feeling dizzy. She has booked an appointment with her GP.

Give **two** physiological measurements that the GP is likely to make and suggest two questions that the GP may ask Milena about her health.

Dizziness can be caused by heart conditions. Think about measurements and questions most relevant to Milena's heart health.

Heart rate

You can feel the heart rate (pulse) in the wrist or neck. It is used to measure how fast the heart beats in beats per minute (bpm). Pulse rate is a physiological indicator of the level of a person's health and physical fitness.

Resting pulse rates

A **resting pulse rate (RPR)** is measured when a person has been still for about five minutes.

The pulse can be measured placing fingers on the inside of the wrist at the base of the thumb and counting the beats for one minute. NHS guidance states that the average RPR for an adult is between 60 and 100 beats per minute. Lower or higher rates are abnormal and may indicate health problems.

Gender – men often have a lower RPR than women

Age – babies and children usually have a higher RPR than adults. For example:
- newborn babies 70–190 bpm
- children aged 5-6 75–115 bpm
- adult 60–100 bpm

Factors that affect RPR

Size – overweight people usually have a higher RPR than lean people

Level of physical activity – fitter people often have a lower RPR pulse rate than less active people. For example, an athlete may have an RPR of 40–60 bpm

Pulse rate during physical activity

Pulse rate increases during physical activity.

✓ The target **maximum** number of heart beats per minute is 220 minus a person's age.

✓ A **healthy** pulse rate during or just after moderate exercise is between 50% and 70% of the maximum.

Recovery after physical activity

Pulse rate gradually returns to RPR after physical activity.

After physical activity, an athlete's pulse rate returns to their RPR more quickly than in someone who is unfit. The athlete has a faster **recovery rate**.

Abnormal readings

Abnormal readings are those above guideline levels when at rest (RPR) or during physical activity. Risks arising from raised pulse rate:

Short-term risks	Long-term risks
👎 dizziness	👎 heart attack
👎 light headedness	👎 stroke
👎 chest pain	👎 high blood pressure

The effects on heath

The heart is working harder to pump blood, so:
- blood vessels may be damaged
- arteries can thicken.

A heart rate which takes a long time to recover after exercise could indicate:
- the heart is working too hard because of high blood pressure
- the heart needs more oxygen than the body can provide, which increases the risk of a heart attack
- the heart isn't working properly because of an undiagnosed medical condition like diabetes.

Now try this

Pauline is 65 and healthy.

1 What should Pauline's maximum RPR be?
2 What is the expected range of Pauline's pulse rate when taking moderate physical activity?

To work out the maximum RPR and healthy pulse rate during or just after physical activity, look back over this page.

Blood pressure

Blood pressure is an important indicator of health. Blood pressure that is too high puts strain on the heart.

Blood pressure readings

Blood pressure is the pressure exerted by blood against the artery walls. It is measured in millimetres of mercury (mmHg) and is shown as two numbers:

- **Systolic pressure** (the top number) is the maximum pressure in the blood vessels as the heart pushes out blood.
- **Diastolic pressure** (the bottom number) is the minimum pressure in the vessels when the heart relaxes between beats.

Blood pressure can increase with stress, so measurements should be taken at least three times and an average recorded.

Published guidance

The NHS and Blood Pressure UK provide charts giving guidance on interpreting blood pressure readings.

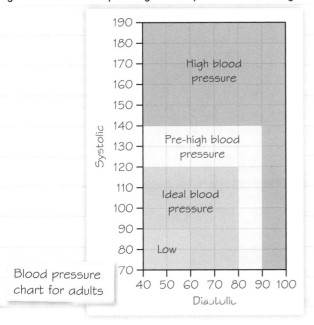

Blood pressure chart for adults

Interpreting readings

☑ Ideal blood pressure is between 90/60 mmHg and 120/80 mmHg.

☑ Pre-high is 120/80 mmHg to 140/90 mmHg.

☑ High blood pressure is between 120/80 mmHg and 140/90 mmHg or above.

☑ Low blood pressure is 90/60 mmHg or lower.

☑ Only one number (systolic or diastolic) has to be higher or lower than the guidelines to be abnormal.

Possible causes of high blood pressure

- Lifestyle – smoking, use of alcohol, drugs (look at pages 9–11)
- Nutrition – unhealthy diet, high salt intake (look at page 7)

Changing to a healthy lifestyle is one of the best ways to reduce blood pressure.

- Genetic inheritance – people can be predisposed to high blood pressure (look at page 2)
- Lack of physical activity (look at page 8)
- Being overweight (look at page 24)

Abnormal readings

High blood pressure

Long term risks of **hypertension** (high blood pressure) are:

- heart disease – the heart has to work much harder to pump blood around the body
- kidney disease – the pressure in the arteries causes them to narrow or weaken, so not enough blood can get to the tissues of the kidneys
- stroke – increased pressure causes blood vessels to weaken, if one bursts in the brain it will bleed into the surrounding tissue
- vascular dementia – narrowing of the arteries in the brain can mean a lack of oxygen and nutrients to the cells, so they begin to die.

Low blood pressure

In many people, **hypotension** (low blood pressure) does not cause health problems and can indicate a healthy heart. However, in some people it may cause dizziness. Low blood pressure can result from health conditions such as diabetes. Low blood pressure can link to aging or result from the use of some medications.

Now try this

Betty's blood pressure reading is 130/85.

Betty cannot change her genetic inheritance, but she can change her lifestyle.

Give **three** recommendations to help Betty lower her blood pressure.

Body Mass Index

Body Mass Index (BMI) is a way of measuring the amount of fat in the body. Being overweight or obese puts a strain on body systems and seriously affects physical health.

Measuring BMI

Health professionals can advise people about lifestyle changes based on their BMI and use readings to track progress. A combination of a healthy diet and exercise helps to lower the risks of being under or overweight. Individuals fall into one of five categories based on their BMI.

Category	BMI kg/m²
Underweight	<18.5
Healthy weight	18.5–24.9
Overweight	25–29.9
Obese	30–39.9
Seriously obese	>40

Limitations

Although BMI is a suitable guide for a healthy weight for most people, it does not take account of:

- waist size – a waist size of more than 94 cm (37 in) for men and more than 80 cm (31.5 in) for women puts individuals at risks to health
- muscle mass – athletes have more muscle and may be heavy for their height
- bone density – this may decrease with age or lack of physical activity
- age – older people may lose muscle and have more fat. For those under 18, BMI is shown on separate charts for boys and girls, with measurements expressed in centiles
- sex – the same chart is used for men and women over 18, although women may have more body fat.

Published guidance

A chart gives the BMI of an individual, using measurements based on their height and weight.

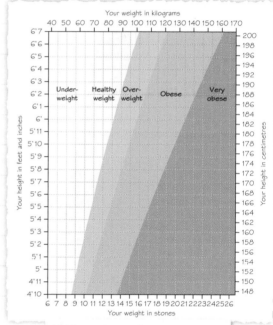

NHS guidance for men and women over 18 years of age.

Risks to health

	High BMI		Low BMI
Long-term risk	**High blood pressure:** As the body gets larger, the heart must work harder to pump blood.		**Slow growth:** Due to a lack of nutrients like protein.
	Heart attack: The arteries in the heart harden due to high cholesterol from fatty foods.		**Osteoporosis:** Bones are brittle and break easily, due to a lack of nutrients like calcium.
	Risk of type 2 diabetes: The body becomes insulin-resistant, so can't reduce blood glucose levels.		**Infertility:** Periods may become irregular or stop (a decrease in calories can stop hormone release).
Short-term risk	**Tire easily; joint pain; breathlessness; snoring** All are due to extra weight and body systems being overworked.		**Skin, hair and teeth problems; tiredness; weakened immune system** All are due to a lack of nutrients and energy from food.

Now try this

In which BMI category are these people?
1 Conran weighs 70 kg and is 1.8 m tall.
2 Sadie weighs 90 kg and is 1.7 m tall.

 Read the information you need from the BMI chart.

Lifestyle indicator – nutrition

Published guidance is there to advise individuals on a healthy and balanced diet.

A balanced diet

A balanced diet means the balance of different food types that a person needs to stay healthy. It contains all the nutrients the body needs in the correct proportions.

fruit and vegetables (at least 5 portions per day)

starchy foods

foods containing protein, such as: meat, fish, nuts, pulses, eggs

dairy products

unsaturated oils, fats and spreads (in small amounts)

Re-read page 7 on nutrition and its purpose.

The Eatwell Guide shows the proportions of each food group you should eat in one day. For example, fruit and vegetables should make up just over a third of a healthy diet.

Fibre and water

As well as a range of nutrients from different food groups, a balanced diet also includes fibre and water.

☑ Fibre is important in the diet to lower the risk of heart disease and maintain a healthy digestive system.

☑ Water is used in all cells, helps regulate body temperature and also aids digestion.

Foods to avoid

unhealthy fats (particularly saturated fats)

Foods high in

sugar (drinks often contain sugar)

salt (no more than 6g per day for adults)

Quantity of food

All foods provide energy but some food types provide more energy than others. Fats provide the most energy, then carbohydrates.

Energy can be measured in calories. The maximum recommended number of calories is about:

- 2,000 kcal for moderately active adult women
- 2,500 kcal for moderately active men.

This includes food and drinks. Exact energy requirements vary according to size (height and weight) and level of activity.

Food labels

Food must be labelled to advise on the amount of calories, fats, sugars and salt because too much of these are unhealthy.

Each burger contains:

ENERGY	FAT	SATURATES	SUGARS	SALT
924KJ	13g	5.9g	0.8g	0.7g
220kcal	MED	HIGH	LOW	MED
11%	19%	30%	<1%	12%

% of an adults reference intake.
Typical values per 100g: Energy 966kJ/ 230kcal

red = high amounts

amber = medium amounts

green = low amounts

Labels also indicate foods suitable for vegans, vegetarians or those with particular requirements such as individuals with coeliac disease who can't eat foods containing gluten.

Now try this

Imran is obese and eats more calories than the recommended daily allowance for men.

1. State **two** types of food Imran should reduce in his diet.

2. State **two** types of food Imran should increase in his diet.

Use the guidance on this page and the nutritional information on page 7.

Lifestyle indicator – physical activity

How much physical activity a person undertakes is a lifestyle choice. Published guidance helps to assess the level of physical activity required to maintain health and wellbeing.

Activity for all

Physical activity guidelines from the UK Chief Medical Officer depend on the age group and the person's ability or circumstance. Activity can be at different levels but is important for all ages and abilities. Activity may be:

* light exercise: walking at slow pace, cleaning/dusting, making a bed
* moderate exercise: hiking, riding a bike, mowing a lawn
* vigorous exercise: aerobics, football, swimming, hiking up a hill.

Benefits of physical activity

Research has shown that taking exercise and reducing inactivity can reduce:

* type 2 diabetes by 40%
* cardiovascular disease by 35%
* falls and depression by 30%
* joint and back pain by 25%
* cancers (colon and breast) by 25%.

Re-read page 8 for more on the positives of physical activity.

Children 1–5 years

Children should aim for at least 150 minutes of activity each day. It should involve different types of activity:

walking — climbing
running — digging
cycling — dancing
throwing and catching

Children and young people 5–18 years

At this age, the advice is to be physically active for at least 60 minutes each day. Activity should:

* be spread evenly across the week
* reduce the amount of inactivity.

Activities should be undertaken that make the child or young person breathe faster and feel warmer.

Adults from 19 years

Adults should undertake each week:

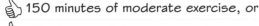

👍 150 minutes of moderate exercise, or

👍 75 minutes of vigorous exercise, or

👍 a combination of moderate and vigorous exercise.

Adults should also undertake exercise on at least two days a week that:

* builds strength (for example gym, yoga, lifting and carrying)
* improves balance (for example dance, bowls, tai chi).

Adults with disabilities

It is important that people with disabilities take regular exercise. Any movement can help to maintain and boost health and wellbeing.

Advice is:

* 150 minutes of moderate exercise each week
* including balance and strength exercises on two days a week.

Now try this

Give **three** more examples of moderate and **three** examples of vigorous exercise for adults.

Look at the examples above and think of different ones. Are there any that you do?

Lifestyle indicator – smoking and substance misuse

Smoking and substance misuse has a negative effect on health and wellbeing. Health and social care workers play an important role in providing advice and support to reduce use.

The role of healthcare organisations

In the UK, healthcare organisations:

- gather data (statistics) about smoking and substance misuse
- identify those most at risk
- analyse data and advise on health risks
- set targets and support people to reduce smoking and drug use
- influence laws that discourage smoking and drug taking.

The statistics

In May 2021, England's Chief Medical Officer, Chris Whitty, said that smoking is likely to have killed more people than Covid-19 in the same period. He estimates that 900,000 people a year die as a result of smoking.

In 2019, there were 4393 deaths from the misuse of drugs.

How common is smoking and substance misuse?

Smoking

Drugs

In 2018, data showed that 14.7% of those over 18 smoked. This was a reduction of 5% from 2011.

Data in 2020 showed that 2.1% of adults aged 16–59 were frequent drug users. Of these, 4.3% were aged 16–24 years.

People make a choice to start smoking and take drugs, but it becomes an addiction. They need support to help them to stop.

Towards a smokefree generation

The Department of Health tobacco control plan aims by the end of 2022 to:

- reduce the number of 15-year-olds who smoke from 15% to 3% or less
- reduce the number of adult smokers to 12% or less
- reduce the prevalence of smoking in pregnant women from 10.7% to 6% or less.

Supporting individuals to achieve aims

Health care professionals will support smokers through counselling, providing aids such as nicotine patches or encouraging electronic cigarettes as an alternative.

Reducing substance misuse

The Government aims to reduce substance misuse by:

- reducing demand – targeting people most at risk
- restricting supply – tackling criminals who supply drugs
- improved treatments and support – making sure the appropriate interventions are made at the right time.

Risk factors for smoking and drug taking

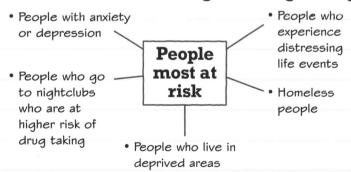

- People with anxiety or depression
- People who go to nightclubs who are at higher risk of drug taking
- People who experience distressing life events
- Homeless people
- People who live in deprived areas

People most at risk

Now try this

Outline the role of healthcare organisations to discourage smoking and drug misuse.

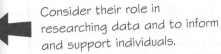
Consider their role in researching data and to inform and support individuals.

Lifestyle indicator – alcohol

Drinking alcohol is a lifestyle choice for many but there is clear advice on ways to minimise risks to health.

The Chief Medical Officer's guidelines

Guidelines are produced from research that shows:

- no amount of alcohol is completely safe
- alcohol increases the risks of cancers such as mouth, throat, breast
- risks are similar for men and women
- heavy drinking leads to accidents, causing head injuries or fractures.

Read page 10 for information on the health risks of alcohol.

Understanding units

A unit relates to the size (volume) of the drink and the amount of alcohol it contains.

- ✓ Small (125 ml) glass of wine = 1.5 units
- ✓ Pint of beer = 3 units
- ✓ Small 25ml (single measure) glass of spirits = 1 unit

Advice on regular drinking

The Chief Medical Officer has advised individuals:

- not to drink more than 14 units per week to keep health risks low
- to spread drinking evenly across a week rather than heavy drinking sessions
- to have alcohol-free days
- not to drink alcohol during pregnancy.

Supporting individuals to achieve aims

Health professionals can help individuals to reduce their alcohol intake or stop drinking through counselling, giving advice on health risks and support for lifestyle changes, or recommending charities.

Higher-risk groups

The Chief Medical Officer has identified individuals who may be as affected more by alcohol:

- young people
- older adults
- individuals with low body weight
- individuals with other health problems
- individuals on medication.

Individuals with lower risk

Women over 55 are less at risk than other groups if alcohol levels are kept to 5 units per week.

Single drinking occasions

There are occasions when individuals may drink more than safe levels. To prevent the risk to health it is recommended:

- to drink more slowly
- to drink with food
- to alternate drinking alcohol with water.

When an individual consumes large amounts of alcohol in a short time, it is sometimes referred to as binge drinking.

Alcohol misuse

Alcohol misuse can be an addiction. Alcohol dependence can happen when a person does not have control over their desire to drink alcohol or the amount they consume.

If a high level of alcohol is consumed in drinking sessions there is an increased risk of accidents, injury and illnesses.

Now try this

Outline the advice that should be given to Sean, Grace and Zara.

Read through the Chief Medical Officer's guidance again to check advice.

- Sean, aged 19, doesn't drink alcohol in the week and drinks no more than 14 units during the weekend.
- Grace is pregnant so she is cutting her alcohol intake to less than 14 units per week.
- Zara, aged 62, has a small glass of wine with her meal three evenings a week.

Person-centred approach

The person-centred approach is holistic and puts the individual at the heart of healthcare planning, so that the whole range of physical, intellectual, emotional and social health needs of an individual are met.

Partnership

In a person-centred approach there must be a partnership between the individual and the health professional. The partnership also extends to include family members and carers.

The approach is rooted in the values (standards or rules) that health professionals must follow.

Health professionals should use a person-centred approach that takes into account an individual's **needs**, **wishes** and **circumstances** when recommending actions for health improvement (a plan to benefit an aspect of health or wellbeing).

Needs, wishes and circumstances

Needs – physical, intellectual, emotional and social health needs.

Wishes – preferences, likes and dislikes, choices, desired health goals.

Circumstances – illness or disability, access to facilities, previous personal experiences, family and relationships, responsibilities.

> **REVISE IT!**
> You might need to use this Component 2 knowledge in your assessment

Benefits of a person-centred approach

Individuals who are in partnership with health professionals will:

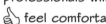 feel comfortable and have trust in a professional who understands them

 be more confident and so more likely to follow recommendations, advice and treatments

 have their unique needs understood and met

 have more control in decision making, which improves independence

 be more motivated to change lifestyle in ways that benefit them

 be more positive about their health and wellbeing.

A family member or responsible person can empower an individual by helping them to express their needs, wishes and circumstances.

Individuals who may need support

Individuals may need support to express their needs, wishes and circumstances because they:

- do not speak English
- have a learning disability
- have dementia
- have hearing loss
- have a mental health disorder.

 Now try this

Kyra is a single mother with two children under three years old. She has been feeling tired, so visited her health centre. BMI results show that Kyra is obese and her blood pressure is slightly raised. After looking at the results, the practice nurse gave Kyra a diet sheet, and told her to follow it and return in one month.

Try to give one example for each aspect – one need, one wish and one circumstance.

Give **three** examples of how the practice nurse could have taken Kyra's needs, wishes and circumstances into account.

Skills and attributes

A combination of skills that are developed through training and experience, and attributes that a person has naturally, both contribute to effective care.

Skills for care

Skills	What it means in practice	Example
Problem solving	Using communication skills to understand the problem. Be able to identify the cause. Make a decision on ways to overcome the problem.	When Gena, a practice nurse visited Tariq, 79, at home he told her that his breathlessness was getting worse. She discussed his medication and found that he had not been taking the required dose. She gave advice and informed his doctor of the concerns.
Observation	Noticing small details, observing changes in behaviour or problems that arise and responding or reporting.	When Sally, a home carer, visited Mike, she noticed that he hadn't eaten the food that had been delivered for him. She encouraged him to eat something and reported her concerns to his GP.
Dealing with difficult situations	Being able to recognise and assess difficult situations, listening and being calm.	When the relation of a service user became angry, Carl listened, remained calm and suggested a way to resolve the problem.
Organisation	Being able to plan and manage own time, resources and space effectively.	Yasmeen planned her visits to the service users and checked that she had the correct information and any resources or aids they required.

Using health care skills

Always:

 think

 look and listen

👍 keep calm

👍 plan.

REVISE IT!
You might need to use Component 2 knowledge about skills, attributes and values in your assessment

Carers must use both skills and attributes so that individuals receive the best possible care.

Attributes that contribute to care

Empathy – being able to understand and share feelings with another person; recognising and having sensitivity to a person's situation

Honesty – being truthful and honest about a person's health needs and treatments; not stealing from others

Attributes

Patience – being able to wait and give time to someone or when carrying out a task without becoming annoyed or angry

Trustworthiness – can be relied on to do the right thing in different situations

Now try this

Look at the photo above.
Explain **two** attributes that the carer should have to carry out his role.

Remember that attributes are what carers should have naturally.

Values in care

All those working in health and social care follow a set of 'values' to ensure the best quality of care.

The quality of care is at the highest level

Makes a positive difference to a person's health and wellbeing

A value-based approach to care

The person's needs are understood and at the centre of decision making

Staff undertake regular training and upskilling

There is anti-discriminatory practice

REVISE IT!
You might need to use Component 2 knowledge about skills, attributes and values in your assessment

The 6 Cs

These are set out in the '6 Cs' for care.

1 Care
- **correct:** providing the correct care that a person needs
- **consistent:** continuing to provide the same level of care throughout a person's life

2 Compassion
- **empathy:** understanding a person's feelings
- **dignity:** valuing a person as an individual
- **respect:** listening to and respecting a person's opinions and feelings whatever their culture or circumstance

3 Competence
- **skills for care:** having the training and skills to provide the correct care
- **knowledge of care:** knowledge about the person, their needs and available treatments and support

4 Communication

With service users, carers and family
- **listening:** and taking into account the person's views
- **discussing:** treatments and support to agree the best way forward

5 Courage
- **confidence to do the right thing:** even when it may be the difficult option
- **speak up if there are concerns:** raise concerns or worries about a person's care or colleagues' practice

6 Commitment
- **to the care of individuals:** continue to provide the best quality of care
- **to improve the experience of individuals:** by continuous development of own skills and knowledge

Now try this

Give **two** examples of ways you can build competence to become an effective healthcare worker.

Refer to the Competence section above and consider what this means for you.

Benefits for health and social care workers

A person-centred approach can also have benefits for those who give support and the services they provide.

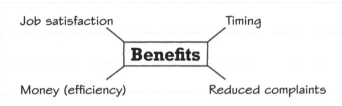

```
Job satisfaction          Timing

          Benefits

Money (efficiency)    Reduced complaints
```

The healthcare worker gets satisfaction by supporting this person's needs.

Job satisfaction

- By building a relationship with the person, morale (self-esteem) is raised for the carer as well as the person.
- The carer gains more fulfilment by meeting the needs and wishes of the person.
- There is less pressure because the person is more likely to follow advice.
- Healthcare workers are more likely to stay in their role, reducing staff shortages that impact on care / waiting lists.

Money

- Early diagnosis of health and development concerns can reduce the risk of more serious illness that would increase costs.
- The person is more likely to have their needs met, so less likely to have to turn to costly emergency services.
- All the person's needs can be addressed and support planned without the cost of visits to different care settings.
- Money is targeted (spent on what people actually need) so there is less waste.

Timing

- Time is spent on what the person really needs and wishes so they are more likely to follow advice.
- A person may have their care needs met at one centre, reducing costs of two or more appointments.

It also saves time for professionals because:

- if a person's needs, wishes and circumstances are understood, they are less likely to be referred to services they won't use
- people may be able to manage their own health without the need to visit support services.

Reduced complaints

People are less likely to complain if:

- they feel respected and listened to
- they are happier because they feel in control of their own care
- their concerns are understood, discussed and addressed early.

Now try this

Give **two** reasons why a person might complain about their care.

 Consider what might happen if care is not person-centred.

Recommendations for a healthy heart

For each goal in a health and wellbeing improvement plan, there must be at least one **recommended action**.

Planning for better health and wellbeing

Making recommendations helps people to reach their goals to reduce blood pressure and pulse rate. Suggested actions must take account of the person's needs, wishes and circumstances.

Here are two examples:

Example	Recommended actions	How it may improve health
Helen's blood pressure is 130/90 mmHg. She leads a busy life and relies on takeaway meals. She visits the gym on Saturdays only.	• Follow the Eatwell Guide. • Reduce take-away meals to one per week. • Take at least 30 minutes exercise each day.	• It may lower Helen's blood pressure to the ideal level between 90/60 mmHg and 120/80 mmHg. • It may reduce the risk of heart disease or stroke.
Vic finds he gets out of breath easily. He smokes and his resting pulse rate is often over 100 bpm.	• Walk to work. • Use nicotine replacement aids such as gum or patches.	• It may improve Vic's resting pulse rate to between 60 and 80 bpm. • It may reduce the risk of respiratory problems, lung cancer and heart disease.

Improving blood pressure

Here are more examples of ways to lower blood pressure:

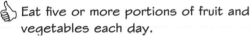 Eat five or more portions of fruit and vegetables each day.

 Cut out salt.

👍 Use techniques such as relaxation dvds.

👍 Join a gym.

 Reduce alcohol consumption.

Improving resting heart rate

Ways to reduce pulse rate and improve recovery time after exercise include:

 taking the recommended amount of exercise of 150 minutes per week

👍 joining an activity group such as dance class or yoga

👍 avoiding caffeine and nicotine

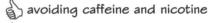 using relaxation techniques.

Yoga is a good way to relax.

Changing behaviour

Recommendations to achieve goals involve changing behaviour.

For example, taking regular exercise, eating healthier foods, eating less, avoiding drugs or nicotine, socialising more or practising relaxation techniques.

Now try this

Give **three** reasons why it is important to take account of a person's needs and circumstances when recommending actions.

 Suggesting vigorous physical exercise for a person with mobility difficulties would be inappropriate.

Recommendations for diet and weight control

There are links between a balanced diet, a healthy weight and physical activity. They should all be taken into account when making recommendations.

Maintaining a healthy body

Nutritious diet

A healthy body

Physical activity

Positive effects of a health improvement plan

People who follow a plan for a physically healthier lifestyle will be fitter, lose weight and have improved self-concept. They will also have lower blood pressure, a healthier heart and reduced risk of cancers.

Example recommendations

During a health review, the practice nurse was concerned that Imani's BMI showed that she was obese. Imani is aged 35 years and single. She often goes for meals with friends. As she leads a busy life, she relies on takeaways most days.

Health concerns	Recommended actions	Support
• Mobility difficulty • High cholesterol • Digestive problems • Increased risk of heart disease	Lower BMI and cholesterol through regular exercise and a healthy diet by: • joining an exercise or dance class • using steps at work, not a lift • cutting down to just one takeaway a week • including five portions of fruit/vegetables each day • replacing sugary snacks with nuts or fruit.	GP and practice nurse Dietician Friends Colleagues

Weight control

Cut down on sugar   Use unsaturated fat and oils

Actions for health and weight control

Use less salt   Follow the Eatwell Guide

Physical activity

Recommendations and actions must be appropriate to the person. A person who is severely obese may need to start with gentle exercise, for example.

Re-read government guidelines for activity on page 26.

Now try this

Explain why it is important for a person with a high BMI to take action through dietary changes and exercise.

Re-read page 7 which gives the relationship between food intake and weight management.

Recommendations for lifestyle changes

Recommendations and actions often focus on improving physical health but can also address unhealthy lifestyles to reduce the risk of ill health.

Reasons for change

A person may wish to change unhealthy aspects of their lifestyle, such as the use of substances, smoking or alcohol because:

- they have a health condition that is caused by or made worse by their lifestyle
- they want to reduce the risk of ill health.

Smoking

Recommended actions for smokers could be:

- nicotine replacement (chewing gum, inhalers, mouth spray)
- medicine
- e-cigarettes.

Recommendations to stop smoking

John, aged 53, is a smoker and has had a persistent cough for three months. His wife doesn't smoke but many of his colleagues at work do.

↓

Health concern: Smoking may lead to lung cancer or heart disease.

↓

Actions:
- Use nicotine skin patches to stop a craving for nicotine.
- Take walks at breaktimes rather than joining colleagues who smoke.

John may need support from a nurse specialist, GP or charity such as ASH (Action on Smoking and Health), as well as encouragement from family and getting colleagues to stop offering cigarettes.

Recommendations for a healthy lifestyle

	Health concern	Recommended actions	Support
Yoko often binge drinks (drinks heavily over a short period of time), which is affecting her work.	• Dependency: becoming alcoholic • Heart disease	• Reduce alcohol consumption to safer limits – under 14 units spread over a week. • Drink water alongside alcohol when out.	Family and friends Charities such as Drink Aware
Kyle is 17 and has started taking drugs when out with friends.	• Mental ill-health: memory and thinking • Risk of injury	• Stop meeting with peers who use drugs. • Attend counselling. • Join a local support group. • Start a new hobby.	Counsellor Family/friends Online charities such as FRANK

Alcohol

Other recommended actions include:

Only drink with food   Change to non-alcoholic drinks

Limit alcohol you buy — **Reduce alcohol consumption** — Let friends and family know and get support

Drugs

Other recommended actions include:

Avoid places and people that use drugs   Use relaxation techniques during cravings

Stop substance misuse — Take regular physical activity

Now try this

Give **two** examples of how friends can support a person who is taking actions to give up smoking.

← It is difficult to give up addictions so people often need the support of friends.

35

Had a look ☐   Nearly there ☐   Nailed it! ☐

Professional support

Health professionals are paid and have been trained to provide support, for example doctors and practice nurses. Formal support includes **primary**, **secondary**, **tertiary** and allied care services.

Primary care services

Primary care services are usually people's first point of contact with health professionals. They include health centres (with GPs, practice nurses and midwives), accident and emergency services, pharmacies, dental surgeries and opticians (both optometrists and opticians).

Service	Functions
Health centre	Measuring and interpreting physiological indicators, such as pulse, blood pressure, peak flow and BMI
	Advising on lifestyle health risks, such as smoking, drugs and alcohol
	Working together with people to produce **health improvement plans** and monitoring progress
	Prescribing drugs and treatments
	Referring patients to other health professionals (secondary and tertiary care services)
Accident and emergency services	Dealing with life-threatening emergencies, such as profuse bleeding, extreme pain, severe allergic reactions, critical burns, stroke and heart attack
Pharmacy	Giving advice on medication
	Offering health promotion and advice
	Providing aids such as nicotine replacement therapies, blood pressure monitors
Dental surgery	Providing treatment for teeth and gums
	Giving advice on how to keep teeth and gums healthy
Opticians	Assessing and monitoring the health of the eyes, and providing glasses
	Giving advice on how to keep eyes healthy

Secondary and tertiary care services

Patients who require hospital care for a health condition will be referred to a secondary care service by their primary health care provider. Tertiary care services provide specialist support in dedicated units, such as stroke rehabilitation, oncology and secure mental health units.

Cardiologist (heart)

Psychiatrist (mental health)

Paediatrician (child health)

Examples of secondary care specialists

Respiratory specialist (lungs and breathing)

Neurologist (brain, spine and nerve)

REVISE IT!
You might need to use this Component 2 knowledge in your assessment

Now try this

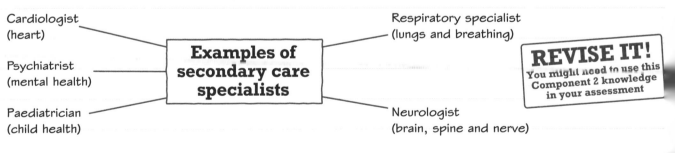

Vincent is worried about his health. He has had a cough and sometimes finds it difficult to breathe. Vincent smokes 10 cigarettes each day.

Smoking can affect blood pressure and pulse. (See also pages 9, 21, 22, 23, 27 and 33.)

Give **two** examples of professionals who might provide support.

Formal support

Allied professionals, trained volunteers, support groups and charities work alongside primary, secondary and tertiary services to provide formal support and specialist advice to help people plan for improvements in health and wellbeing.

Allied health roles

Allied health professionals can help individuals make health improvement plans and support them in achieving their goals. Some allied health professionals can also diagnose conditions in their specialist area.

Service	Functions
Dietician	Advises on risks of an unhealthy diet and benefits of a healthy diet, and on diets to help manage certain conditions
Physiotherapist	Advises on exercise and movement for people with breathing or mobility problems, may provide mobility aids
Art or music therapist	Provides support for people with emotional and communication problems
Speech and language therapist	Works with people with communication difficulties to improve communication skills
Advocate	Speaks on behalf of people who are not able to express their wishes
Domiciliary care worker	Supports older people and people with disabilities with everyday care in their own homes
Clinical support staff	Health care assistants, dietetic assistants and phlebotomists (specialist blood collectors) who may also be involved in formal support

Types of formal support

Formal support can take many forms:

- **Physiological measuring aids**, such as blood-pressure testing kits or weighing scales for people to monitor change themselves.
- **Practical support**, such as healthy menu plans, suggested exercise DVDs and routines.
- **Advice and leaflets on lifestyle health risks**, such as recommended alcohol levels.
- Introductions to **support groups**, such as those shown in the table opposite.
- **Emotional support**, such as providing encouragement to achieve targets.

Volunteers

Trained volunteers support professionals and other support staff in a wide range of roles from such as listening, advising and encouraging individuals.

Other organisations that provide formal support

Some charities and organisations provide specialist support and advice in particular areas. Some run support groups.

Area	Example organisation
Alcohol	Alcoholics Anonymous
Diet	Weight Watchers
Diet and exercise	Change4Life
Smoking	Action on Smoking and Health (ASH) QUIT
Drugs	Action on Addiction Talk to Frank
Social isolation of older people	Age UK

Now try this

Explain why physiological measuring aids, such as blood pressure testing kits and weighing scales, can help people to meet their health improvement plan targets.

If people can see their own progress they are more likely to achieve their targets.

Informal support

Informal support is provided by people who are not paid to provide help.

Informal support providers

People are more likely to be successful in following a health improvement plan if they have the support of the people who are closest to them. It can be hard to make lifestyle changes if family and friends do not also change their behaviour.

People who could provide informal support are:

- partners
- family members
- friends
- neighbours
- work colleagues
- community.

Partners

Partners can give support by:

- following the same health plan, such as taking exercise or stopping smoking
- praising progress and complimenting improvements
- providing reassurance when it is hard to stick to the plan and encouragement to resume the plan if necessary
- helping overcome barriers to following the plan, such as giving financial or practical support. For more information on barriers and obstacles see pages 39 and 45.

Family support

For many people, partners and family are an important source of informal support.

Lifestyle change	Family members can ...
Lose weight	help to prepare low-fat meals, stop buying takeaways and unhealthy snacks
Improve financial management	research money advice services, suggest alternative sources of income, such as benefits
Do more exercise	suggest opportunities for walking rather than taking the car, take up a sport or an active hobby the family can do together
Stop smoking	stop smoking near the person, agree not to smoke in the home, stop buying and offering cigarettes
Stop using drugs	research support services, accompany the person to appointments, give encouragement

Friends, neighbours and community

Friends can also be helpful in providing support and encouragement.

Lifestyle change	Friends can ...
Lose weight	join a fitness programme together, attend a support group together, give mutual encouragement, share low-calorie snacks
Reduce alcohol to recommended limits	reduce their own alcohol intake, offer non-alcoholic alternatives at social occasions, suggest social activities that do not involve alcohol
Become less isolated	visit regularly, accompany the person or invite them to social events
Quit smoking or smoke less	also quit, stop offering cigarettes
Take more exercise	go on runs and walks together, take up joint activities such as dance classes or tennis

Now try this

Copy and complete the table below by including examples of informal and formal support.

Goal	Informal support	Formal support
Eat more healthily		
Quit smoking		
Become less isolated		

Re-read pages 36 and 37 to remind yourself of types of formal support.

Barriers to accessing identified services

Barriers are unique to the health and social care system. They prevent individuals from accessing services.

Possible barriers to accessing services

There are lots of reasons why people may have difficulty accessing services. The role of the health professional is to anticipate and identify potential barriers and to recommend ways to overcome these.

Type of barrier	Possible barrier	Recommendations
Geographical	👎 Service is difficult to get to because of poor bus or train services	👍 Arrange hospital transport 👍 Suggest telephone helplines or internet support groups
Financial	👎 Charges to use the service 👎 Time off from work would mean loss of pay	👍 Check for entitlements, such as free medicines and treatments 👍 Direct the person to advice on benefits and employee rights
Psychological	👎 Fear of being judged because there is stigma around a health problem (mental health, obesity)	👍 Talk about concerns and reassure 👍 Direct the person to a charity that supports people with a particular health problem
Physical	👎 Difficulty getting into the building where the service is provided (no wheelchair access) 👎 Nowhere to park near the service	👍 Be aware of services that are adapted for easy access 👍 Ask a friend or family member to drop the person at the service
Cultural needs	👎 Communication difficulties because English is an additional language 👎 Social or cultural background is not understood	👍 Use anti-discriminatory practice and encourage others to do so 👍 Provide support such as a family member or advocate (a person who can express the person's views or wishes)
Personal needs	👎 People with a sensory disability 👎 Difficulties because of a speech or language impairment	👍 Provide ease of access to information such as hearing loops, large print, braille and support such as BSL signers 👍 Invite a family member or advocate for support
Resources	👎 Limits on services, such as support aids and equipment 👎 Staff shortages, leading to long waits for appointments and support	👍 Suggest sources of second-hand equipment 👍 Look for alternative strategies, for example an exercise DVD if there are no places at an exercise class

Now try this

Madge has a health improvement plan goal of losing weight with a target to lose 1 lb each week for three months. She has two recommended actions:

- to join a dance class, but she is embarrassed to attend because of her weight
- to get advice from a dietician at the local hospital, but getting there is difficult because of limited transport links.

Suggest **two** ways that Madge can overcome the barriers for each of the recommended actions.

REVISE IT!
You might need to use this Component 2 knowledge in your assessment

Think of two examples for each action.

Had a look ☐ Nearly there ☐ Nailed it! ☐

Potential obstacles

Obstacles are things that are personal to an individual and block them from moving forward. Obstacles can prevent them from taking actions or make actions more difficult.

Examples of obstacles

Health professionals must be aware of a range of obstacles to progress.

Type of obstacle	Examples
Emotional/psychological	Low self-concept, lack of motivation, acceptance of current health and wellbeing situation
Time constraints	Lack of time because of work and study commitments or family responsibilities
Availability of resources	Lack of financial resources, equipment or opportunities
Unachievable targets	Targets that are too ambitious, not broken down into small steps or have unrealistic timescales
Lack of support	Lack of **informal** support from family and friends, lack of **formal** support, not able to access support services

REVISE IT!
You might need to use this Component 2 knowledge in your assessment

A person-centred approach

If a person-centred approach is used to devise a health and wellbeing improvement plan, obstacles are less likely to arise as the plan will be tailored to the person's:

- **needs** – recommended actions will be suitable
- **wishes** – if the person wants to make improvements they are more likely to succeed
- **circumstances** – their abilities and time constraints.

If a person-centred approach is not used, the plan will not take into account the person's level of motivation, time issues, resources, support structures, age, gender, culture and ability, and obstacles in any of these areas could prevent progress. See page 29 to remind yourself of the person-centred approach.

Mitigation

Obstacles can be prevented from occurring by knowing as much about the person as possible when devising the plan.

Obstacles that arise during implementation of the plan can be mitigated, for example:

- **Emotional** – offering encouragement and pointing out progress
- **Time** – suggesting ways to fit new activities into daily routines
- **Resources** – suggesting sources of second-hand equipment or providing resources to borrow, pointing out free classes or an outdoor gym
- **Support** – encouraging family to be supportive, suggesting formal support groups
- **Specific** – adjusting the plan to the individual's own needs, wishes and circumstances.

Now try this

Give **three** reasons why a person-centred approach helps health professionals to overcome possible obstacles when planning actions for health improvements.

Think of a reason related to each of these aspects: needs, wishes and circumstances.

Emotional and psychological obstacles

A person's emotional and psychological (mental) state influences their motivation and affects their confidence in their ability to follow a health improvement plan and reach their target.

Motivation

Motivation is the drive to continue with something. It is usually higher at the start of a new health and wellbeing improvement plan, when results can show more quickly. Over time, people may find it harder to maintain their commitment to the plan.

Lack of motivation

Reasons for a lack of motivation could include:

- a conflict between choices such as worrying that giving up smoking could result in weight gain
- other priorities in a person's life – such as getting married or bereavement
- having a negative attitude – believing change will be too difficult
- lack of progress, for example losing weight quickly in the first weeks, but then slowing down
- having a 'blip' – thinking there is no point in continuing the plan after a brief return to an old lifestyle, such as smoking a cigarette after giving up.

Self-concept

People with poor self-concept don't value themselves. They may feel powerless to change their lifestyle or that there's no point in starting because the task seems too big.

Some people think that because they have not been successful in other aspects of their life they won't achieve their health goals.

People with poor self-concept may not feel they have support and approval from family and friends, even if they really do.

Acceptance of current state

People may:

- accept their present health problems or lifestyle choices, as it is easier to stay the same than to make changes
- have no incentive to make a change because they do not understand the health risks
- have no desire to change, for example if they are happy with their weight or don't want to give up smoking.

Overcoming emotional obstacles

Health professionals can help people by recommending actions to overcome emotional and psychological obstacles.

Staying motivated	• Suggest new ways to meet people, such as voluntary work to prevent isolation • Plan rewards, such as buying new clothes after dropping a clothing size • Record the money saved by not smoking or drinking less alcohol
Building self-concept	• Make sure targets are achievable (Look at SMART targets on page 44) • Break down targets into small steps so that progress can be seen • Give reassurance, encouragement and regular feedback on progress
Challenging acceptance of the current state	• Encourage the person to think about the possibility of change • Help the person understand the longer-term health risks of staying the same and the benefits of making change

Now try this

Harri has been following a diet and exercise plan to reduce his BMI. He made good progress in the first three weeks, but is struggling to get back on track after Christmas.

Think about how festivities make it hard to stick to the plan, and how this could cause Harri to lose motivation.

Give **three** reasons why Harri may have lost the motivation to follow his health and wellbeing improvement plan over Christmas.

Time constraints

A major obstacle to achieving health improvement targets is time. Health professionals must understand an individual's time constraints and recommend actions that take them into consideration.

Possible time constraints

Lack of time is a big obstacle to a healthy lifestyle.

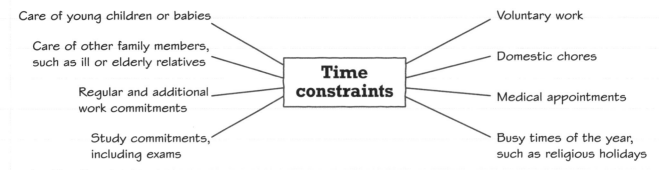

Care of young children or babies

Care of other family members, such as ill or elderly relatives

Regular and additional work commitments

Study commitments, including exams

Time constraints

Voluntary work

Domestic chores

Medical appointments

Busy times of the year, such as religious holidays

Making time for physical activity

Health professionals can help people to fit exercise into their routines by suggesting:

1 regular, convenient times to exercise and clubs to join, such as Zumba or 'New to running'

2 how exercise can be incorporated into the daily routine, for example by walking or cycling to work, or getting off the bus one stop early

3 exercising while watching TV, for example using an exercise bike or doing lunges and planks during the adverts

4 exercising at home using a DVD or mobile phone app.

Everyone who works at a desk should take regular time out to stretch arms and legs.

Making time to eat healthily

Cooking healthy meals doesn't have to take up a lot of time. Health professionals can share ideas such as:

- cooking a healthy casserole or soup in a large quantity and freezing portions
- using quick and healthy recipes from supermarkets or the internet.

Support

Health professionals can help people understand that they do not have to do everything themselves. Individuals might need to delegate for the sake of their own health. Getting supportive family members to take on more tasks helps to free up time – drawing up a family rota can be a good idea.

Now try this

Josh, aged 16, is studying GCSEs and has a part-time job. He has reached an unhealthy weight, often going to a fast-food place at lunchtime. He has agreed actions that include at least one hour of daily exercise and eating a balanced diet.

Think about how family members could help Josh, as well as how he can find time himself.

Give **three** suggestions that would help Josh find time to follow his plan.

Availability of resources

Many people need resources to be able to carry out the recommended actions in their health improvement plans. Resources may be financial, such as payment for fitness classes, or equipment, such as weighing scales or a peak flow meter.

Financial obstacles

Carrying out recommended actions may incur additional costs.

Financial obstacles can include:

- gym membership, entry fees for a swimming pool or leisure centre
- cost of attending fitness classes
- costs of travel to the gym or pool, or to attend health appointments
- cost of travel to a social group
- higher costs of some healthy foods.

REVISE IT!
You might need to use this Component 2 knowledge in your assessment

Lack of facilities or equipment

People face obstacles if they do not have the necessary resources to support actions.

Individuals who live in rural locations may not have access to pools, gyms and fitness classes, or to social support groups.

It is not possible to track health improvements without access to health monitoring equipment, such as weighing scales or blood pressure monitors.

People may need access to equipment for exercise at home, such as DVDs, weights and exercise balls.

Those who wish to stop smoking may need supplies of nicotine patches and gum.

Overcoming obstacles

Anticipating obstacles and recommending actions for their mitigation is part of the health improvement planning process. Recommendations include:

Obstacle	Recommendation
Lack of access to fitness facilities (cost or location)	• Some councils run free fitness classes for people with particular health issues, like obesity or heart problems • Run, walk or take up gardening • Use free fitness phone apps or DVDs
Cost of healthy food	• Look for price reductions and special offers in supermarkets • Cook food instead of buying ready meals • Cook in bulk and freeze portions • Make packed lunches instead of buying lunch out
Cost of transport	• Combine visits to the health centre with other trips (for example, shopping) to reduce travel costs • Share lifts to social clubs with others
Lack of equipment	• Use weighing scales at the local pharmacy or sports centre • Borrow fitness DVDs from the library or buy at a charity shop • Look for second-hand equipment

Now try this

Paulo's goal is to lower his BMI through physical activity. He lives rurally and doesn't have access to a gym.

Think about ways to become more physically active without access to special facilities.

What **three** pieces of advice could be given to Paulo to overcome these obstacles?

Unachievable targets

Short-term and long-term recommendations and actions for health improvement must be achievable or people will give up trying to reach them.

Reasons

There are various reasons why targets may be difficult to achieve:

- expectations are set too high
- targets are not clear
- there are too many targets
- timing is wrong
- targets are not suitable for the individual
- fear of not being able to meet targets
- not being in the right frame of mind to commit to the plan, perhaps due to depression.

Any target that is not SMART (specific, measurable, achievable, realistic and time-related) will become unachievable.

❶ High expectations

If targets are set too high, they will be unachievable. People will be reluctant to start the plan if they feel they can't succeed, or they may give up when they fail to see progress towards the target.

Unrealistic expectations arise when:

- planned targets do not allow enough **time** – people need time to make changes, for example gradually reducing the number of cigarettes smoked rather than quitting immediately
- planned targets are too **large** – large weight-loss targets may be daunting. Step-by-step weight loss is healthier and more sustainable
- planned targets cause **anxiety** – expecting a person to socialise in a large group may be overwhelming. Meeting with individuals or in small groups could be the first step.

❷ Unclear targets

Targets must be clearly defined. The person will give up if they don't know what they need to do.

People with communication or learning difficulties may require special presentation of their targets, so that the information is clear to them.

❸ Too many targets

Multiple targets are overwhelming. People don't know where to start if they are expected to change different aspects of their lifestyle all at once.

Stopping smoking, reducing alcohol intake and losing weight at the same time could be unachievable.

❹ Poor timing

Both the **start time** of the plan and **time allowed for each target** will affect the person's chances of success. Targets may be unachievable if:

- the start date of the plan is inappropriate – stopping smoking or drinking alcohol may be more difficult during the holiday season
- there is not enough time to achieve each target.

❺ Unsuitable targets

Targets must be suitable for each individual person in order to be achievable. An exercise plan for an older person with mobility difficulties will be very different from one for an active younger person.

Now try this

Use each of the five headings on this page relating to why targets may be unachievable. Give **one** way in which each type of obstacle could be overcome.

Use the examples given on the page to help you think of ways to minimise obstacles.

Lack of support

The level of support from family and friends has an impact on the success of a health and wellbeing improvement plan.

Lack of family support

A major obstacle to success is lack of support from family. Family members may:

- continue an unhealthy lifestyle, for example not being physically active
- make unhealthy food choices, for example buying unhealthy foods and fizzy drinks, and ordering takeaways
- smoke
- drink alcohol over the recommended level or binge drink
- not understand health risks of lifestyle choices or the benefits of making changes
- not encourage the person.

Lack of peer support

It is difficult to keep to a plan if friends put temptation in the way.

Recommendations

Health professionals can try to include partners and family members when planning actions with a person, so the whole family understands the risks of not making lifestyle changes and the benefits of sticking to the health and wellbeing improvement plan. It is important to explain the obstacles the person may face and the ways in which the family can give support. This might include suggesting meal plans that the whole family can enjoy or practical ways in which family members can help, such as by taking on chores to free up time to carry out the plan's actions. (See page 38.)

> **REVISE IT!**
> You might need to use this Component 2 knowledge in your assessment

Encouraging support

Health professionals can guide family and friends to offer appropriate support.

Family members can:

👍 also adopt healthy lifestyles

👍 be encouraging

👍 buy healthy foods

👍 make sure there are no unhealthy foods in the home

👍 give practical or financial help.

Friends can:

👍 plan alcohol-free nights out

👍 stop offering cigarettes or recreational drugs

👍 join a sport or hobby club together

👍 motivate by complimenting achievements.

Now try this

Steve, aged 68, lives alone. He has a sister and a son living nearby. Since his wife died two years ago, Steve has neglected himself. This has resulted in frequent infections. When visiting his GP, Steve agreed a health and wellbeing improvement plan with a target to improve his personal hygiene.

← Steve's poor personal hygiene may have isolated him from his family, leaving him without support.

Give **two** reasons why Steve's family may find it difficult to support him to achieve his target.

Your Component 3 set task

Component 3 will be assessed through a series of questions which will be set by Pearson and externally marked. In some questions you will be asked to make an assessment of the healthcare needs of different service users using case studies.

Revising your skills

Your assessed task could cover any of the essential content in Components 1, 2 and 3. You can revise the Component 3 content in this Revision Guide. This skills section is designed to **revise skills** that might be needed in your assessed task. The section uses selected content and outcomes to provide examples of ways to apply your skills.

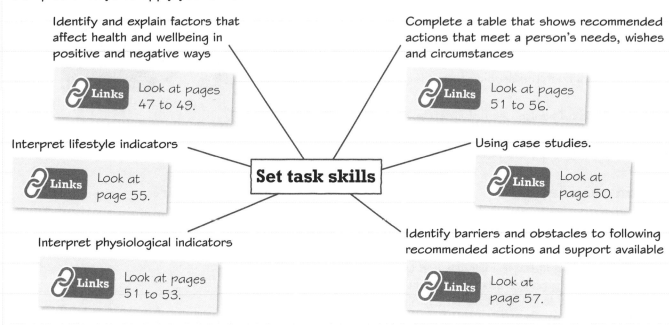

Identify and explain factors that affect health and wellbeing in positive and negative ways

🎧 **Links** Look at pages 47 to 49.

Complete a table that shows recommended actions that meet a person's needs, wishes and circumstances

🎧 **Links** Look at pages 51 to 56.

Interpret lifestyle indicators

🎧 **Links** Look at page 55.

Set task skills

Using case studies.

🎧 **Links** Look at page 50.

Interpret physiological indicators

🎧 **Links** Look at pages 51 to 53.

Identify barriers and obstacles to following recommended actions and support available

🎧 **Links** Look at page 57.

Check the Pearson website

The activities and sample response extracts in this section are provided to help you to revise content and skills.

Ask your tutor or check the Pearson website for the latest **Sample Assessment Material** and **Mark Scheme** to get an indication of the structure of the actual assessed task and what this requires of you.

The details of the actual assessed task may change, so always make sure you are up to date.

Now try this

Visit the Pearson website and find the page containing the course materials for BTEC Tech Awards Health and Social Care. Look at the latest Component 3 Sample Assessment Material to check:

- the structure of your set task and whether it is divided into parts
- how much time you are allowed for the task, or for different parts of the task
- what briefing or stimulus material might be provided for you
- any notes you might have to make and whether you can take selected notes into your supervised assessment
- the activities you are required to complete and how to format your responses.

Identifying factors

You may be asked to identify factors that affect health and wellbeing from a list. These examples are multiple-choice questions.

Identify **one** social factor that can affect health and wellbeing.

☐ A religion
☐ B alcohol use
☒ C bullying
☐ D employment

Some questions do not require a written response. You choose the correct answer from a list you are given. Write a cross (X) in the box next to the answer you think is correct.

The student has correctly identified that **bullying** is a social factor. Religion is incorrect as it is a cultural factor, alcohol use is a lifestyle factor and employment is an economic factor.

Read multiple choice-questions carefully and try not to jump to conclusions. If you are not sure, try to eliminate (rule out) answers you know are incorrect.

Try not to take too much time on these answers. If you are not sure go back to them later.

These questions draw on your knowledge of types of factors. You can re-read information about factors that affect health and wellbeing on pages 2–20.

Some questions may ask you to identify more than one factor. Read the questions carefully so that you know if you need to put a cross (X) in one or more boxes.

Identify **two** effects of mental ill health.

☒ A stress
☐ B obesity
☐ C type 2 diabetes
☒ D anxiety

Stress and anxiety are both effects of mental ill health. Obesity and type 2 diabetes are types of physical ill health.

If you put a cross in the wrong box, put a line through like this and put a cross in the right one.

Now try this

Identify **two** positive effects of cultural identity on health and wellbeing

☐ A insecurity
☐ B participation
☐ C high self-esteem
☐ D isolation

Culture refers to the customs, beliefs, identity and practices of groups of people.

Explaining factors with negative effects

You may need to **identify**, **give**, **state** or **explain** factors that have negative effects on health and wellbeing. 'State' and 'give' mean that you have to provide information about the negative effect. 'Identify' means that you need to select the correct answer from the information given. 'Explain' means you need to give a reason why the factor has a negative effect.

Identify **two** negative physical effects associated with smoking.

- ☒ emphysema
- ☐ liver disease
- ☐ type 2 diabetes
- ☒ heart attack

If you are asked to identify factors or health conditions make sure that you indicate the most likely answer(s).

Reread page 9 on the effects of smoking.

State **two** negative effects of noise pollution on health and wellbeing.

You may be asked for one or two examples. Make sure you give the required number so that you don't lose any marks.

Sample response extract

Hearing loss
Loss of sleep

These questions require a phrase or one-sentence answer. This student has correctly identified that noise pollution can affect hearing and the ability to sleep.

Explain **two** negative effects on a child of a high level of parental conflict.

Questions may ask you for one or more examples.

If you are asked to explain, you must give an effect and go on to give reasons for that effect.

Sample response extract

A child may have physical symptoms such as headaches because they are anxious and stressed.

A child may not be able to sleep because parents' noise keeps them awake at night.

Using the words 'because' or 'so' after the example will help you to give a full answer. This student has given sound reasons why a child may get headaches or be unable to sleep.

Now try this

Explain **two** negative effects that discrimination has on emotional wellbeing.

A person will feel left out or not as important as others.

Explaining factors with positive effects

Some questions may ask you to **identify**, **give**, **state** or **explain** positive effects of factors, life events or circumstances.

Give **one** positive effect that social inclusion can have on the emotional wellbeing of an individual.

Remember the 'PIES' classification. You could be asked about Physical, Intellectual, Emotional and Social factors.

Sample response extract

Being included can improve self-esteem.

Links   Revise effects of inclusion on page 13.

Sample response extract

Improves mobility
Helps to maintain a healthy weight

You may be asked for one or two examples. Make sure you give the required number so that you don't lose any marks.

State **two** positive effects of regular physical activity on health and wellbeing.

This question requires a phrase or one-sentence answer for each effect. The student correctly identifies that exercise improves flexibility and strengthens muscles and is good for weight control.

Explain **two** positive emotional effects that starting college can have on a student.

The question states that the student must explain **emotional** effects. This student has done this successfully because they include examples that focus on how the student may be feeling.

Sample response extract

A student may have higher self-esteem because they are progressing in their education.
A student may feel happy because they feel included in a new group of friends.

Be sure to read the question carefully in case it specifies the type of effect your answer should cover.

Now try this

Explain **two** positive effects that starting college may have on a student's health and wellbeing.

It might help you to think about your own emotional responses when starting school or college.

Responding to case studies

Some questions ask you to respond to information about a specific person. Case studies can tell you about a person's health and lifestyle.

> During a recent health review, Naomi has been told that her BMI is 29 kg/m², which means she is overweight.

Explain **one** potential risk of being overweight on Naomi's health and wellbeing.

A case study introduces you to the person and could give information about a physiological or lifestyle indicator. You will need to use the information given to help you answer the question.

To answer this question you will have to identify one possible risk and give reasons.

 Links Read page 24 to revise the effects of a high BMI.

Make sure your answer focuses on the individual in the case study.

Sample response extract

One possible risk is high blood pressure because her heart has to work harder.

> Her GP wants to support Naomi to lose weight. She finds that Naomi is single. Naomi has just been promoted at work, which meant moving away from family and friends to a new flat. Naomi has a desk job and works long hours. She likes to chill and watch TV and eat snacks when she gets home.

Assess how Naomi's lifestyle could affect her ability to follow recommended actions to lose weight.

This section of the case study gives more information about Naomi's lifestyle and circumstances. It tells us that Naomi may sometimes feel isolated as she doesn't live near friends and family. She is physically inactive at work because she has a desk job. Her diet is poor because as she works long hours she just likes to relax at home.

Reviewing case studies

When responding to a longer case study it helps to:
☑ read it through twice
☑ underline key phrases as you read the case study as shown here to help you answer the question.

Remember, you can go back and look at the case study again while answering the questions.

Sample response extract

Naomi may not be able to prepare healthy meals because she works long hours. She may find it easier to continue to eat unhealthy snacks. Working long hours also means it will be difficult for her to take regular physical exercise. Support is also important. Because Naomi doesn't have family close by, she won't get the type of support and encouragement she needs to lose weight. Time constraints and lack of support may affect her ability to stick to a plan for healthy eating and physical activity.

This student has used all the information from the case study to assess Naomi's lifestyle. They have given careful consideration to what they know about her and made a judgement, coming to a conclusion about how Naomi's lifestyle might affect her ability to lose weight.

Now try this

Use the case study to explain **two** possible positive effects lowering her BMI could have on Naomi.

Read through each of the two parts of the case study about Naomi.

Explaining physiological indicators – BMI

You may be asked to respond to a question about physiological indicators such as BMI and demonstrate knowledge of how it impacts on a person's health and wellbeing.

State the correct classification for BMI 18.5–24.9 kg/m².

 **Sample response extract**

Healthy weight

 Links Revise classifications for BMI, blood pressure and pulse rates on pages 22-24 to help you answer questions in your assessment.

This is correct and the weight that a person should strive to achieve.

Complete Table 1 by:

(i) stating **three** actions that the practice nurse could suggest that will improve Naomi's health and wellbeing

(ii) giving **three** ways these actions could improve Naomi's health and wellbeing.

This question relates to the case study on page 50 about Naomi.

The student has used information from the case study to understand Naomi's needs, wishes and circumstances

Sample response extract

Table 1

	Three actions	Ways the actions could improve Naomi's health and wellbeing
1	Exchange unhealthy snacks for fresh fruit	Lower her BMI to a healthy level
2	Naomi could join a dance class	Reduce the risk of high blood pressure
3	Provide a Tai Chi or yoga DVD	Increase activity and improve mobility

Treat these questions like an 'Explain' question: state the action in the first column and then expand on this in the second column. In this case, by explaining the way the action could improve Naomi's health and wellbeing in the second column.

Explain the possible effect of lowering her BMI on Naomi's emotional development.

Sample response extract

Naomi's self esteem may be higher if she loses weight because she is more confident with her body image.

The student has explained and not just stated in their answer. They have identified the possible effect (self-esteem). They go on to explain the reason for the effect (increased confidence).

Now try this

State the BMI range for someone who is classified as 'obese'.

Refer to page 24 to find BMI classifications.

Explaining physiological indicators – pulse

You may be asked to interpret data on a service user's resting pulse rate, predicted maximum pulse rate during exercise and recovery rate, and give a clear and detailed explanation about their current health and any possible physical health risks.

State **two** positive factors that may affect a pulse rate.

Read the question carefully. Check the number of answers you need to give and whether you need to consider positive and/or negative effects.
In this question you need to give two examples of **positive** effects.

Sample response extract

a healthy diet
being physically active

You will not get any marks if you give two negative effects.

State the NHS guidance for the average RPR (resting pulse rate) of an adult.

Sample response extract

60–100 bpm (beats per minute).

This student has clearly shown they know the range of a normal pulse rate. Remember that it may differ in children and athletes.

When Dev visits his health centre, he finds his resting pulse rate reading is 101 bpm.

Explain **two** possible long-term risks of a high pulse rate on Dev's physical health.

Long-term risk is something that will have a serious effect on health and wellbeing.

 Links Re-read the normal heart rate (pulse) on page 22.

Sample response extract

In the long term, Dev is at risk of a heart attack because his arteries may thicken. He may have a stroke because the blood vessels to his brain have weakened.

The student shows they understand that Dev's pulse is higher than normal readings. They use what they have learned about the possible effects a high pulse rate may have on health and wellbeing.

Now try this

Give **two** possible short-term risks of a high pulse rate.

Read page 22 for short-term risks of a high pulse rate.

Explaining physiological indicators – blood pressure

You may be given a person's blood pressure readings. Knowing the classifications – low, ideal, pre-high and high – will help you to answer questions about the level of risk to their health and wellbeing.

> The nurse took this reading of Seema's blood pressure 130/85 mm Hg.

State the classification for Seema's blood pressure.

Blood pressure readings

Readings show two numbers. Systolic at the top shows the maximum pressure as the heart contracts to push blood into the arteries. Diastolic at the bottom shows the minimum pressure in the arteries between heart beats.

Remember, only one number (systolic or diastolic) has to be higher or lower than normal to be an abnormal blood pressure reading.

Sample response extract

Seema's blood pressure is in the pre-high range.

⬅ The student does not need to explain the effects, but just state the classification.

> Seema recently moved to a new flat in a large city after the breakdown of her marriage. She's started to drink more alcohol than the recommended 14 units each week, which has increased her weight to an unhealthy level.

Assess the effect of Seema's lifestyle on her health and wellbeing.

⬅ This tells you more about Seema. Information about the person's lifestyle will help you explain or assess the reasons for blood pressure that is outside the ideal range.

To **assess** something, you need to carefully consider all the factors or events in the information you've been given and identify which are relevant to the question. In this case, these are Seema's lifestyle and the effect it might have on her health. You should make a judgement on their importance and come to a conclusion.

Sample response extract

Seemas's blood pressure may be in the pre-high range. This may be because Seema's heart is working too hard because she is overweight. Her blood pressure may also be raised because she is drinking more alcohol than advised. She may be stressed about her marriage breakdown. In the short term, she may feel dizzy and experience chest pains. If she does not change her lifestyle, her blood pressure may become higher still, increasing her risk of heart disease and stroke.

This student has used the information given to assess why Seema's blood pressure is higher than the ideal. They have considered the factors and made a judgement on how Seema's lifestyle is affecting her health and wellbeing, increasing the risks to her future health.

Finally, the student has come to a conclusion on the possible effects to her health if she does not change her lifestyle.

Now try this

Give **two** actions that Seema could take that could help to lower her blood pressure.

 Re-read the case study to see how Seema could change her lifestyle.

Explaining social and cultural factors

You may be given more information about a person in a case study and asked to explain the possible social and emotional effects of additional factors that may affect their health and wellbeing.

> Howard is from the Jewish faith. Before he moved, he lived in an area where there was a strong Jewish community. He was an active member of the synagogue where he knew many people and would stay to talk to them after each service.

 Links Revise information about social factors on page 13 and cultural factors on page 14.

This information discusses a cultural and religious factor that could have a positive or a negative effect on Howard. Both approaches could be valid.

If asked about effects of social and cultural factors, make sure you specifically link to these aspects of wellbeing. You might mention social interactions, relationships, self-image and feelings.

Explain **one** negative effect of moving away from his community on Howard's wellbeing.

Sample response extract

Howard has lost the social interaction that he had with the Jewish community, which is likely to have a negative effect on his emotional and social wellbeing because he no longer has the feelings of safety and security he developed through friendships and companionship.

If you are asked to explain the effects of social factors on wellbeing you could answer like this.

This response focuses on the social aspect of friendships and social inclusion, and the emotional impact of the loss of social contacts.

Explain **one** positive effect of Howard's faith on his health and wellbeing.

Sample response extract

Having a strong faith is likely to have a positive effect on Howard's emotional and social health and wellbeing because it may help him deal with worries and stress and give him a feeling of contentment.

This response focuses on the importance of Howard's religion and shared beliefs, and how that may help him to overcome negative factors.

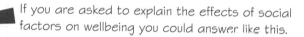

Now try this

Explain another negative effect of not being able to practise his faith on Howard's social and emotional wellbeing.

 Consider how not being able to attend his synagogue may impact on Howard's feelings about himself and his ability to socialise.

Interpreting lifestyle indicators

You may be given information about a person's lifestyle, relating to nutrition, smoking, alcohol consumption, substance misuse or inactivity. You will need to interpret the data accurately, making direct reference to published guidance.

Josh drinks around 14 units of alcohol, but only drinks on his weekend off.

This introduces Josh and tells you about his alcohol consumption.

Describe how occasional heavy drinking could affect Josh's health and wellbeing.

Sample response extract

Josh does not drink more than government recommended 14 units each week but he drinks this at weekends. Drinking heavily over a short time could lead Josh to become alcohol dependent. It may contribute to an increase in his weight. In the future, it would increase his risk of cancers, liver and heart disease.

The learner shows that they understand research data about recommended levels of alcohol consumption and the risks of not following guidelines.

For a describe question, you just need to give an account of something. You don't need to include a reason.

🔗 **Links** Look back at page 28 to remind yourself about alcohol and lifestyle indicators.

Josh has been complaining of back pain. He tries to visit the gym each week but at other times takes little exercise.

Assess how Josh's inactivity could affect his health and wellbeing.

Sample response extract

Josh is inactive most of the week but does attend the gym once a week. According to recommended exercise levels, he should take 150 minutes of exercise spread over the week, so his visit to the gym may not be enough to help maintain his physical fitness and may be the cause of his back pain. Not getting enough exercise may result in a loss of lung capacity and reduction in stamina, leading to a raised pulse or blood pressure when he does need to exert himself. Inactivity can lead to obesity and joint pain, and increase his risk of diabetes and heart disease.

If you are asked to assess lifestyle data, you could answer like this. You must give details of the factors and come to a conclusion about the possible effects on the person's current physical health and wellbeing, and risks to their future physical health.

The student gives details about Josh's level of physical activity. They make links to government guidelines in order to interpret the information. They refer specifically to Josh's existing health condition (back pain) when explaining risks and then also give examples of other possible increased risks to health.

🔗 **Links** Look back at page 26 to remind yourself about lifestyle indicators and physical activity.

Now try this

Josh's friends are trying to persuade him to use recreational drugs. State **two** effects of substance misuse on Josh's health and wellbeing.

Any use of recreational drugs can affect health. Re-read the information about substance misuse on page 11.

Recommendations and actions

You could be asked to suggest actions for a service user. Health and wellbeing recommendations and actions should be person-centred, so that they take into account the person's needs, wishes and circumstances.

> Kesh, aged 15, enjoys sport but gets out of breath and tires very easily. He misses breakfast but goes to the local fast-food shop at lunchtime. Kesh has low self-esteem because he is overweight and wants to lower his BMI.

Read the case study information carefully so that you can suggest actions based on Kesh's needs, wishes and circumstances.

Complete the table below by:

- stating **three** actions that the school nurse could suggest that will improve Kesh's health and wellbeing
- giving **three** ways these actions could improve Kesh's health and wellbeing.

Sample response extract

Action	Ways the action can improve Kesh's health and wellbeing
Take gentle exercise 15 minutes each day.	It will increase his lung capacity.
Take a healthy lunch box to school.	It could reduce his weight.

Because Kesh gets out of breath easily, the student has recommended he starts with regular gentle exercise. This will improve his lung capacity so he can breathe more easily. The student understands that visiting the fast-food shop regularly can only increase Kesh's weight. Cutting out fast food and eating more healthily will reduce his weight.

You may be asked about the types of support individuals may need to help them improve their health and wellbeing.

Explain **two** ways that support can improve the health and wellbeing of Kesh.

 Revise information on types of support on pages 36–38.

Sample response extract

A dietician could help Kesh to plan more nutritious food for his lunchbox that he is more likely to enjoy and eat.

A parent could encourage and praise Kesh so that he continues to take exercise each day.

These explanations clearly show how each example of support is 'person-centred'. In the first example, the student refers to providing food that Kesh is likely to eat. The student also realises that because Kesh has low self-esteem praise will be important and likely to help him stick to the plan.

Now try this

Give **two** reasons why it is important to take into account a person's wishes.

 Re-read the information about a person-centred approach on page 29.

Understanding barriers and obstacles

As a healthcare professional, you must be able to understand the possible barriers and obstacles the service user might encounter when carrying out the recommended actions. You should be able to suggest how to overcome these.

> Tom is 82 years old and lives alone in his 4th-floor flat. Tom had a stroke recently which has left him with speech impairment and mobility difficulties. He has to rely on public transport to attend speech therapy and physiotherapy at the local hospital.

Explain **two** barriers that could prevent Tom from improving his health and wellbeing.

Barriers prevent a person from accessing the service. How would it affect you if you couldn't express yourself? You may not consider travelling alone difficult, but is a barrier for a person aged 82.

Sample response extract

Tom's recent stroke left him with a speech impairment, which may prevent him from expressing his wishes.

Tom has to rely on public transport to get to his hospital appointments, so may find difficulty in travelling alone to the hospital because of his reduced mobility.

When considering barriers, try to put yourself in the position of the person.

You may be asked to give or describe ways to overcome barriers. An example might be to arrange for an advocate to support Tom to express his wishes and transport to get him to the hospital.

> Tom has been depressed since his partner's death last year. He feels isolated because he has no family living close by.

Explain **two** obstacles that could prevent Tom from improving his health and wellbeing.

An obstacle can block a person from taking actions and moving forward.

Sample response extract

Tom's depression may deter him from attending his speech therapy and physiotherapy regularly, which will delay his improvement.

Tom may lack motivation to improve because he will not have support and encouragement from a partner or family who live close by.

For each example, the learner has given the obstacle and then used connective words like 'because' and 'which' to help explain how that obstacle could prevent Tom from improving his health and wellbeing.

Now try this

State **two** barriers that a person with hearing loss may face when accessing services.

Think about how hearing loss would impact your use of services, such as booking/attending appointments.

Answers

The answers provided here are examples of possible responses. In some cases, other answers may also be possible.

1. Health and wellbeing

This means understanding and meeting a person's physical, intellectual, emotional and social needs.

2. Inherited conditions

Individual responses but an example could include:
- **Physical** – mucus damages her lungs, affecting her breathing and mobility.
- **Intellectual** – Gemma sometimes misses school because of the condition, affecting her learning.
- **Emotional** – she may have poor self-concept because of feeling different and could be frustrated by her inability to live a normal life.
- **Social development** – the condition reduces her opportunities to socialise and make friendships.

3. Physical ill health

Individual responses but answers could include:
- heart attack
- angina
- heart failure.

4. Mental ill health

Individual responses

5. Physical abilities

Individual responses but answers could include two from this list:
- personal care such as washing and dressing
- preparing food such as opening jars or cans
- writing.

6. Sensory impairment

Individual responses but answers could include two from this list:
- unable to communicate with others
- has lost confidence and self-esteem
- finds difficulty in building friendships with others.

7. Nutrition

Individual responses but answers could include three from this list:
- healthy immune system
- healthy teeth
- healthy skin
- healthy eyes
- healthy hair.

8. Physical activity

Answers should include one from each of the areas:
- **Physical** – low energy, obesity, stiffness of joints
- **Intellectual** – poor memory, reduced thinking skills
- **Emotional** – stress, poor self-concept, depression
- **Social** – isolation, poor social skills, fewer opportunities for social interaction

9. Smoking and nicotine use

Individual responses but an answer could be as follows:
Being unable to stop smoking may lead to poor self-concept. Smokers may worry about the negative effects on their health and about financial pressures because of the cost. Smokers may feel socially isolated when they have to leave social spaces to smoke outside. People may avoid smokers because of the smell of their hair, breath and clothes.

10. Alcohol misuse

Individual responses but answers could include:
- lack of concentration
- have low self-concept
- may feel ill / have headaches.

11. Substance misuse

Individual responses but answers could include two from this list:
- breakdown in relationships with his family
- aggression, which may lead to trouble with the police
- poor self-concept
- suicidal feelings.

12. Relationships

Individual responses may include:
- boosting self-concept
- giving confidence
- providing security and support
- sharing experiences leading to feelings of happiness and contentment.

13. Social interaction

Individual responses but answers should include one example of direct and indirect discrimination, harassment and victimisation.

14. Cultural factors

Individual responses but answers could include:
- men may feel they need to show they are strong
- they may not want to speak to a female health worker about a condition that affects men.

15. Economic factors

Individual responses but an answer could be as follows:
The status of an occupation affects a person's self-concept. High-status jobs help people to feel valued and low-status jobs may make them feel less valued.
The status of employment can affect the level of income. Higher income can result in a feeling of financial security, and lower income in a feeling of insecurity.

16. Environmental factors – housing

Individual responses but an answer could include the following:
- **Physical** – respiratory disorders, colds and flu, asthma, infections, unfit through lack of exercise, heart disease
- **Intellectual** – difficulties in concentration, unable to study
- **Emotional** – anxiety, depression
- **Social** – pressure on relationships, social isolation

17. Environmental factors – pollution

Individual responses but answers could include two from this list:
- Neville was breathing traffic fumes when he lived in a city
- he is likely to have breathed harmful fumes at work
- he has been exposed to his wife's cigarette smoke (passive smoking).

18. The home environment

Individual responses but answers could include three from this list:
- showing aggression
- behaviour changes
- often complaining of physical symptoms
- frequent bruises or burns
- anxiety
- low self-esteem
- being underweight.

19. Life events

Individual response but the answer should include one negative and one positive example from the lists:
- Negative: reduced mobility; a decline in memory; physical pain/illness
- Positive: more opportunity/time to socialise and spend time with family; able to pass on the wisdom and guidance that comes with life experience to their children/grandchildren.

20. Life circumstances

Students' own responses of the impact on them when experiencing a change in circumstances.

21. Health indicators

Individual responses may include:
Physiological measurements:
- pulse
- blood pressure.

Questions (two from this list):
- How many units of alcohol do you consume each week?
- Do you smoke?
- What is your level of physical activity?

22. Heart rate

1   100 bpm
2   Between 78 and 93 bpm

23. Blood pressure

Individual responses but could include three of the following. Betty could:
- give up or reduce smoking
- cut down her salt intake
- take regular physical activity
- reduce her alcohol intake
- avoid stressful situations.

24. Body Mass Index

1   Conran: healthy weight
2   Sadie: obese

25. Lifestyle indicator – nutrition

1   foods high in sugar, high in fats
2   fresh fruit; fresh vegetables

26. Lifestyle indicator – physical activity

Individual responses but answers could include three from the moderate list and three from the vigorous list:
- Moderate: dancing; a brisk walk; doubles badminton; general gardening; painting/decorating; water aerobics
- Vigorous: sports such as squash, cross country, hockey; using gym equipment such as treadmill; martial arts; dance aerobics.

27. Lifestyle indicator – smoking and substance misuse

Individual responses but answer could include the following:
- Gather and understand the data around the number of people who smoke or misuse drugs.
- Influence laws to discourage smoking or drug taking.

- Give information on health risks. Encourage and support people to stop through counselling, medicine and aids.

28. Lifestyle indicator – alcohol

Sean is drinking no more than 14 units a week, but he should spread his drinking over the week or drink less at the weekend. He may be more affected by alcohol because he is young. Grace should not drink alcohol because she is pregnant. Zara's drinking is well within the recommended levels, meaning no advice is necessary.

29. Person-centred approach

Individual responses but answers could include:
- Needs – the nurse should listen to Kyra to find if she has other less obvious needs, for example physical, intellectual, emotional or social issues, that could be making her tired.
- Wishes – the nurse should discuss different diets with Kyra to find which one she would prefer and which one she thinks fits best with her lifestyle.
- Circumstances – the nurse should ask how Kyra is managing alone with two young children and consider the effects of stress on her diet and blood pressure.

30. Skills and attributes

Individual responses but answer should include two from this list:
- empathy to understand how the person feels when having difficulty standing or walking
- patience if the person needs time to stand/move
- trustworthiness so that the service user feels safe and comfortable in his care
- honesty because he should always give an honest response to her questions and should not take anything belonging to her.

31. Values in care

Individual responses but answers could include:
- undertaking training
- gaining experience in a healthcare setting.

32. Benefits for health and social care workers

Individual responses but answers could include two reasons from:
- they may not feel that their views have been taken into account
- they feel they are not being respected
- their healthcare worker hasn't listened or responded to concerns they raise

33. Recommendations for a healthy heart

Individual responses but answers could include:
- to know if the actions are appropriate by understanding their lifestyle and culture
- to know if a person is physically able to carry out the actions
- to know if they have any dietary or cultural needs that might prevent actions from being taken.

34. Recommendations for diet and weight control

Individual responses could include:
There are two ways to create a calorie deficit: diet and exercise. It is easier to do both in moderation than one more intensely i.e., doing a 500 calorie exercise and eating 250 less calories may be easier than trying to eat 750 less calories.

35. Recommendations for lifestyle changes

Individual responses but answers could include two from this list:
- not buying or offering them cigarettes
- reminding them how it will benefit their health
- praising them for achievement
- not smoking near them.

36. Professional support

Individual responses but answers could include two from this list:
- a pharmacist
- Health Centre (GP or practice nurse)
- a respiratory specialist.

37. Formal support

Individual responses but answers could include:

Using a blood pressure testing kit or weighing scales can help a person monitor their progress as they work towards their target. Individuals are motivated when they see progress

38. Informal support

Individual responses but answers could include:

Goal	Informal support	Formal support
Eat more healthily	Family	Dietician, Weight Watchers
Quit smoking	Partner	GP, QUIT
Become less isolated	Friends	Domiciliary care worker, Age UK

39. Barriers to accessing identified services

Individual responses but answers could include two of:
- Madge could get a dance DVD to follow at home.
- Madge may feel more confident if a friend or family member goes to dance class with her.
- Madge could be given a diet sheet with meal plans.
- Madge could speak to the dietician via a video link.

40. Potential obstacles

Individual responses but answers could include:
- If needs are understood, actions can be recommended that are suitable and achievable.
- If a person's wishes are taken into account, they are more likely to take responsibility for following the plan.
- If personal circumstances are considered, the plan will fit in with time constraints and around other commitments.

41. Emotional and psychological obstacles

Individual responses but answers could include three from this list:
- Harri did well at the beginning of the plan but has seen his progress slow down.
- His family are usually supportive, but during Christmas they provided lots of treats instead of healthy food.
- He's not followed the diet plan during Christmas and may feel there's no point in starting again.
- His self-concept may be poor if he feels he is not succeeding in his plan.
- Christmas events took priority in his life, so he wasn't able to follow the exercise plan.
- He may be finding the exercise routines or diet plan boring.

42. Time constraints

Individual responses but answers could include:
- Josh could join a school team to exercise in his lunch break.
- Josh's family could help him by making a healthy packed lunch to take to school, creating time for him to exercise at lunchtime.
- Josh could get up earlier to walk or cycle to school, instead of using a bus or being driven in a car.

43. Availability of resources

Individual responses but answers could include the following. Paulo could:
- run in his village park
- buy a fitness DVD from a charity shop
- use an app for a fitness programme on his mobile phone.

44. Unachievable targets

Individual responses but answers could include:
1. High expectations – discuss with the person what they feel they could achieve within a certain time.
2. Unclear targets – be specific about what has to be done and talk through each target to check the person understands.
3. Too many targets – focus on one lifestyle aspect to change at a time.
4. Poor timing – take into consideration what is happening in the person's life, for example holidays and celebrations, when agreeing a start date.
5. Unsuitable targets – match targets and actions to a person's level of ability.

45. Lack of support

Individual responses but answers could include the following. Steve's family:
- may not understand how Steve's personal hygiene is affecting his health
- may avoid him because of his poor personal hygiene rather than giving him encouragement.

46. Your Component 3 set task

Individual research.

47. Identifying factors

B participation
C high self-esteem

48. Explaining factors with negative effects

Individual responses but answers could include:
- having low self-esteem because of a lack of confidence in own abilities or culture
- feeling depressed because a person does not have the same opportunities as others.

49. Explaining factors with positive effects

Individual responses but answer could be two from:
- emotional impact because of improved confidence, self-esteem
- social impact because they have the opportunity to build new friendships
- intellectual impact because they are extending knowledge and learning and developing new skills.

50. Responding to case studies

Individual responses but answers could include:
- Naomi may have higher self-esteem because she feels more confident about her weight
- Naomi may find she has more energy so is able to take part in activities when she gets home from work.

51. Explaining physiological indicators – BMI

30–39 kg/m^2

52. Explaining physiological indicators – pulse

Individual responses but answers could include two from:
- lightheadedness
- dizziness
- chest pain.

53. Explaining physiological indicators – blood pressure

Individual responses but answers could include two from:
- eat a balanced diet
- increase the amount of fruit and vegetables in the diet
- use relaxation techniques, e.g. relaxation tapes, mindfulness
- reduce alcohol to less than 14 units per week.

54. Explaining social and cultural factors

Individual responses but answers could include:
Being unable to practice his religion in a place of worship may leave Howard feeling disconnected from his faith and spirituality. He might feel isolated now he's not part of that community. It could lead to isolation, loneliness and low self-concept.

55. Interpreting lifestyle indicators

Individual responses but answers could include two from:
- kidney damage
- breathing problems
- liver damage
- HIV or hepatitis (from shared needles)
- poor self-concept.

56. Recommendations and actions

Individual responses but answers could include:
- They are more likely to follow the actions.
- They will have more trust in the person who supports them.

57. Understanding barriers and obstacles

Individual responses but answers could include:
- The person may not understand what the health professional is saying to them.
- The person may not be able to discuss their needs/wishes.

Notes

Notes

Notes

Notes

Notes

Notes

Notes